RAMP

RISK ANALYSIS AND MANAGEMENT FOR PROJECTS

a strategic framework for managing project risk and its financial implications

Institution of Civil Engineers and the Faculty and Institute of Actuaries

THE INSTITUTION OF CIVIL ENGINEERS

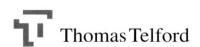
Thomas Telford

Published for The Institution of Civil Engineers and the
Faculty and Institute of Actuaries by Thomas Telford
Publishing, Thomas Telford Ltd, 1 Heron Quay,
London E14 4JD.
www.thomastelford.com

Distributors for Thomas Telford books are
USA: ASCE Press, 1801 Alexander Bell Drive, Reston, VA
20191-4400, USA.
Japan: Maruzen Co. Ltd, Book Department, 3–10
Nihonbashi 2-chome, Chuo-ku, Tokyo 103
Australia: DA Books and Journals, 648 Whitehorse Road,
Mitcham 3132, Victoria

First published 1998
Reprinted 1998
Revised, 2002

A catalogue record for this book is available from the
British Library

ISBN: 0 7277 3200 5

Designed and typeset by Kneath Associates, Swansea
Printed and bound in Great Britain by Hobbs the Printers,
Hampshire

Foreword

Risk surrounds every human activity and influences everything we do. RAMP (risk analysis and management for projects) is a process which has been developed by a joint working party of the actuarial and civil engineering professions, for the purpose of evaluating and controlling risk in major projects. RAMP demonstrates how to identify, analyse and mitigate risks, and how to place financial values on them. It aims to achieve as much certainty as possible about a long-term and uncertain future. Once allied with sound judgement it should reduce the chance of the resources committed to a project being wasted or, indeed, the project being a failure. This should lead to better financial returns for sponsors, investors and lenders.

The RAMP process is concerned not only with the construction phase of a project, important though that is. It covers the entire life-cycle of the asset, with regular risk reviews at key points and a system for the control of those risks which remain. It includes not only 'hard' projects involving the construction of a physical asset, but also 'soft' projects such as the acquisition of a business or the launch of a new product or service, or the running of an existing long-term business or activity.

Although RAMP was developed with major projects in mind, its principles are also applicable to smaller projects. The depth of analysis might well be curtailed for such projects, and simplifying assumptions may be made, but the thought process required is identical.

Some aspects of RAMP will already be familiar to those readers who have previously worked on major projects. This is because the members of the working party controlling the development of RAMP already had extensive experience in the field and in addition they visited some major undertakings to learn about current practices.

Even experienced readers will gain value from this handbook, if only because of the way it sets the various processes within a comprehensive framework of engineering and financial considerations and presents a logical path through a complex maze. The handbook is likely to be of use to everyone who is concerned with the financial, commercial, legal or engineering aspects of major projects and ongoing activities of any kind.

This is a revised edition of the handbook. Attention is particularly drawn to the new Appendix 7, which presents the RAMP process in a simple form.

Adrian Long
President of the Institution of Civil Engineers
2002-3

Jeremy Goford
President of the Institute of Actuaries

Tom Ross
President of the Faculty of Actuaries

STOP PRESS

Just as this revised edition of the RAMP Handbook was going to press (July 2002), HM Treasury published a Consultation Document and supporting materials on the appraisal and evaluation of policies, programmes and projects in the public sector. The current Treasury guidance, issued in 1997, is contained in a publication known as the Green Book. The new proposals aim to tackle the following deficiencies in the current process:

- The methodology needs to be long-term and to tackle key issues, such as the evaluation of benefits.
- There need to be stronger incentives to encourage users to adopt a systematic and thorough approach to appraisal.
- There needs to be strengthened expertise on appraisal techniques within government.

The most striking proposal is that the discount rate used to appraise projects should be reduced from 6% to 3½% p.a. This will have the effect of placing a greater value than at present on benefits received and costs incurred in future years, particularly in respect of more distant periods. Another proposal is that a specific adjustment should be made in the appraisal to allow for 'optimism bias', i.e. a systematic tendency which has been observed for appraisers to be over-optimistic in assessing projects. This adjustment will be based on an analysis of past experience. However, if project appraisers can demonstrate that good practice has been adopted (i.e. that the risk areas contributing to optimism bias have been effectively managed) then the adjustments may be reduced.

We are pleased to see that RAMP is recommended by HM Treasury as a tool for identifying and managing risk (see page 40 of new draft Green Book). This follows a description of RAMP in a Review conducted by the Government's consultants (Mott MacDonald), where RAMP is described as a proven method for managing project risks.

The overall thrust of the Treasury's new proposals is to answer the question, 'Is this objective worth the resources which would be spent on it?' We believe two other key aspects are, 'Which risks ought to be mitigated?' and 'How can the residual unmitigated risks be controlled once the project commences?' RAMP will help to provide the answers to all these questions. Projects will then not only be well selected but will also have the best chance of being delivered effectively, to time and within budget.

RAMP can equally be applied in the private sector.

July 2002   Chris Lewin
                   Chairman, RAMP Working Party

References

The following documents can be found on HM Treasury's website:

http://www.hm-treasury.gov.uk/greenbook.

- The Green Book – Consultation Paper. Appraisal and Evaluation in Central Government.
- The new draft Green Book (Main Text and Annexes)
- Review of Large Public Procurement in the UK, July 2002, a report by Mott MacDonald.

Acknowledgements

This handbook has been written by a working party jointly supported by the Faculty and Institute of Actuaries and the Institution of Civil Engineers. The Chairman of the working party is Chris Lewin. The other members in 1998 (when the first edition of the handbook appeared) were: Professor Chris Chapman, Michael Clark, Professor Robert Clarkson, Clare Delmar, Nigel de Rivaz, Peter Hansford, Terry Mulroy, Mike Nichols, Jonathan Readings, Professor Tony Ridley, Owen Simon, Mark Symons, Luke Watts and Graham Withers.

The following are thanked for the helpful advice and assistance given to the working party: Jim Armstrong, Mike Casebourne, Richard Chapman, Dr Sheila Farrell, Sheila Grande, Clive Hopkins, John Kerman, Punit Khare, Ian Reeves, Richard Tollis, Professor Sir Frederick Warner and Brian Weavin.

The working party owes a special debt of gratitude to Mike Nichols and The Nichols Group Limited for the great contribution they made in this initiative, to Owen Simon for undertaking the considerable task of editing the first edition of the handbook and to Mark Symons for his service as Secretary of the working party.

The current (2002) members of the working party are: John Bennett, Professor Chris Chapman, Professor Robert Clarkson, Peter Dingwall, Philippa Foster Back, Professor Patrick Godfrey, Chris Lewin, Mike Nichols, Gerald Orman, Professor Tony Ridley, Brian Robinson, John Ryan, Mark Symons and Luke Watts.

Contents

Introduction and summary

1.1 Introduction

This handbook describes a process for analysing and responding to risks which can affect the overall success of projects. The process is called RAMP – standing for 'risk analysis and management for projects.' It has been devised by a joint working party of the Institution of Civil Engineers and the Faculty and Institute of Actuaries.

In 1994 the two professions decided to establish the joint working party, consisting of experienced actuaries, civil engineers and economists, to develop a better way of looking at project risk and controlling it effectively. Both professions found that they had fundamentally the same very practical approach to risk, although sometimes using different terminologies to describe the basic concepts. By pooling their skills, knowledge and experience, derived from applying well-established techniques in widely different circumstances, they were then able to produce a risk analysis and management process which went beyond the risk methodologies in common use by any one of the professions represented on the working party. It is hoped that the result can be extensively applied in a wide variety of projects to optimise decision making.

The handbook presents the RAMP process and acts as a guide to its use. Flow charts and brief notes on techniques which can be applied are set out in the Appendices. This chapter starts with the rationale and context for RAMP and is followed by an overview of the RAMP process (Chapter 2), which includes an outline of the basic concepts and principles of risk. The RAMP system is explained in detail in Chapters 3 to 8. Some applications and case studies are discussed in Chapter 9 and opportunities for future development of RAMP in Chapter 10. There is a glossary and bibliography.

The eleven appendices to the handbook provide in-depth guidance to some of the key concepts and methodologies which underpin the RAMP system, including the meaning of risk (Appendix 1) and ways to model investment (Appendix 2). The main steps in the RAMP process are summarised in Appendices 9 and 10 for ease of reference.

Some readers may prefer to start with a case study and they should turn straight to Appendix 7.

RAMP is designed to meet a perceived need for a more rigorous approach to risk management which can be applied to all types and stages of investments – e.g. investments in new railways, manufacturing plants, property developments, telecommunications networks, computer systems and new services. RAMP provides a method to enable a structured and consistent analysis of risk within projects (and between them) to be carried out effectively. It can be applied either at a strategic level or as a detailed analytical and control process.

1.2 A summary of RAMP

RAMP is a comprehensive and systematic process for identifying, evaluating and managing risks in capital investment projects. It covers the entire life of a project from inception to close-down, not just the construction stage. The process consists of four activities.

Activity A:	Process launch
Activity B:	Risk review
Activity C:	Risk management
Activity D:	Process close-down.

The first activity launches the RAMP process. An individual specialist or, if the investment is large, a team is appointed to implement the RAMP process. The 'baseline' objectives, scope and plans for the project are defined, as well as the underlying assumptions on which these are based.

The next activity is a risk review, which is repeated at key stages or decision points throughout the life of the investment. This involves systematically identifying risks and entering them in a risk register. Next the risks are evaluated to determine their likelihood and impact, and any relationships between them. Where appropriate, mitigation measures are identified to avoid, reduce or transfer risks. These measures are incorporated in a risk mitigation strategy. For those risks which remain, an investment model is used to estimate the overall riskiness and viability of the project. Assuming the project is not aborted, a risk response plan is then prepared.

The third activity, risk management, is conducted between risk reviews as part of the mainstream management of each stage in the life of the investment. This involves implementing the risk mitigation strategy and risk response plan developed during the preceding risk review. Activities and events during the progress of the project are monitored to identify new or changing risks. Then appropriate measures are taken to deal with them. Designated individuals, called risk custodians, are charged with managing the risks which fall within their areas of responsibility.

The last activity is the closing down of the RAMP process, when a retrospective review is made of the investment in terms of its success in meeting its objectives, and the effectiveness of RAMP in contributing to the outcome.

1.3 Importance of risk

All projects or business ventures involve risks of various kinds. This applies to the smallest domestic project, such as the construction of a garden shed, as much as it applies to very big projects costing many millions or billions of pounds like new toll bridges, under-sea links, mass transit railways, motorways and airports. In recent times there have been many examples of major projects which have either been abandoned before becoming operational, cost up to twice the budgeted amount to construct, opened twelve months late, performed well below the specified level of reliability or generated less than 50% of the forecast annual revenue. As a consequence, governments, funders and lenders have become extremely reluctant to accept the risks inherent in such investments. The scope for projects to go disastrously wrong does not vary with their size: a simple project like the aforementioned construction of a garden shed can provide just as much risk as a project many times bigger, even though the consequences of the failure of such a project might be trivial compared with the catastrophic costs associated with the failure of a major project, such as the terrible sinking of the *Titanic* in 1912 which caused the deaths of over 1600 people.

Some readers may be surprised that the *Titanic* is described as a 'project' at the time it sank, even though it had by then entered the operating phase. The reason is that we use the word 'project' to encompass the whole investment life-cycle of an activity, not just the construction phase. In the case of a ship, the project commences when the idea of building the ship is first conceived and ends when the ship is no longer in operation and disposed of. We also apply the word 'project' to any organised business activity where an investment is made, whether it involves the creation of a physical asset or not.

There may also be some surprise that the word 'failure' is used to describe the sinking of the *Titanic*. In the civil engineering profession 'failure' normally means a structural failure of the physical asset, leading to its being damaged or even destroyed. However, we are looking here at investments in terms of their overall lifetime performance, measured against the original objectives (as modified from time to time). If these objectives are not achieved, the project as a whole will usually have failed – even though the physical asset may still be intact. It is this emphasis on the whole investment life-cycle, and on the overall picture rather than the physical asset alone, which is one of the main characteristics of RAMP.

In practice, it is virtually impossible to avoid all risks. They can often be reduced and can sometimes be transferred – e.g. through contracts, financial agreements, concessions, franchises and insurance policies – but there is usually some residual risk. For example, the prime contractor or concessionaire can become insolvent and consequently not fulfil its obligations.

There is a growing realisation that the key to success in investments is not to ignore or be intimidated by risk, but to analyse and manage it effectively. One of the major advantages of risk analysis and control is that it allows profitable opportunities to be exploited which would otherwise be judged too risky. Another advantage is that it leads to positive action to minimise the risks of adverse events as far as is practicable and economic. Risk is often most efficiently managed by arranging for it to be carried by the party best able to understand and control each risk at the lowest cost.

1.4 Weaknesses of existing approaches

There are a number of shortcomings in current methods of dealing with project risk, including

- inadequate follow through from the analysis stage to the control of risks once the project starts to be implemented
- a concentration on risks in asset creation rather than on the potentially higher risks in other stages of the investment life-cycle (especially the operating stage)
- a tendency to focus on risks which can be most easily quantified, without the exercise of proper judgement to get a good feel for the other risks involved
- too little attention to changing risk exposures during the investment life-cycle
- no satisfactory method for combining risks – especially where, as often is the case, the separate risks are interdependent
- a lack of consistency in analysing and dealing with risks for different projects.

As a consequence

- projects are not consistently analysed even for the same sponsoring organisation and different standards of analysis are applied
- clients, investors and other interested parties cannot rely on the results of risk analysis
- risks which were identified for mitigation can remain unmitigated
- no satisfactory framework exists for developing a record of experience concerning specific categories of risk and the associated outcomes
- there is no reliable basis for auditing risk analysis and management
- research and expertise is largely fragmented and dispersed instead of contributing cumulatively to improve the state of the art.

Because no other satisfactory, commonly accepted and comprehensive approach exists, the working party decided to embark on the development of RAMP in order to overcome the above weaknesses.

1.5 The need for RAMP

A survey by the Confederation of British Industry (CBI) in 1994 showed that only about one-quarter of manufacturing companies used quantitative methods to assess project risk, with the majority relying on subjective judgement. There was evidence that some companies were using a very high minimum acceptable rate of return (i.e. 'hurdle rate') to judge the acceptability of projects, in the hope that this would provide a built-in contingency margin to cover risk. They probably did not realise the dangers in doing this. While it is appropriate to use a higher hurdle rate for projects having a particularly high degree of risk which is incapable of specific analysis and mitigation (for example, the risks associated with investment in a developing country with an unstable political regime), it is entirely inappropriate to do so for the majority of risks which are not only capable of analysis as described here but are also often capable of mitigation. A failure to carry out proper risk analysis will often lead to some of the possibilities of risk mitigation being left unexplored. Another danger of blindly using too high a hurdle rate without proper risk analysis is that it could easily lead to the incorrect acceptance of high risk projects which may have large returns in some circumstances and the incorrect rejection of low risk projects with good returns but which fail to meet the artificially high hurdle rate.

Later surveys have confirmed the 1994 findings. Although reductions in interest rates have led to the use of somewhat lower hurdle rates, the features described above still remain.

It seems likely that increasing attention will be paid to the appraisal and discussion of capital projects, both at their outset and once they are in operation. Rigorous analysis of the resource implications and the benefits and disbenefits will include a review of the wider considerations such as pollution, use of scarce resources, disruption for third parties, safety, social benefit, etc. In particular it will become increasingly unacceptable to waste the world's scarce resources on projects which turn out to be a failure because the risks were inadequately appraised at the outset.

With increased dependence on advanced technology and complex infrastructure systems, the assessments of large new projects will inevitably become a more complicated process than when less advanced facilities could be built on 'greenfield' sites. Not only will the physical constraints and technological challenges become more demanding but there will be the need to take account of a much wider range of vested interests and often some powerful voices which are opposed to the project. There will be a greater range of risks to be considered and the quantification of the risks will become even more difficult. The RAMP process will help to ensure that all additional work necessary to meet these new challenges is undertaken in the optimum manner.

1.6 Special features of RAMP

The particular characteristics of RAMP include the following.

- It is a logical process, designed to provide a useful and practical framework for the identification, analysis, mitigation and control of the risks inherent in a complex activity.
- It *must* be supplemented by good judgement and common sense throughout: these are crucially important inputs. RAMP provides a framework within which sound judgements can potentially be made but it does not explain how they can be made and it certainly should never be used as a substitute for them.
- It is designed to evaluate all major risks over the life-cycle of a project, including the vital revenue risk – i.e. the risk that the net revenue stream from a project may vary significantly from that which has been forecast.
- It is disciplined and needs to be applied carefully, with a proper follow-through from one stage to another, so that all the major issues get addressed.

- It can be viewed as an outline route map, which will be filled out with project specific detail, in order to become useful to a variety of parties (who may each look at it from a different perspective).
- It pays special attention to disaster scenarios, even if the probability of occurrence is low.
- It links with investment models which place suitable financial values on the assessed risks, and highlights the key risk areas which must be kept under review in future.
- It shows the *order* in which the various stages of the appraisal process should be carried out, so as to keep the unnecessary work to a minimum.
- It ensures that there is a strong linkage between the initial risk assessment process and the process for controlling the risks in practice once the project has reached the implementation phase.

To underline the need to apply RAMP with good judgement and common sense, it must be understood that it is not a comprehensive guide to every aspect of project appraisal. If it is used to provide a numerical result mechanically, without thought, then the process will have been misused. It can never provide reliable results if the data used as input is unreliable – 'garbage in, garbage out' applies to RAMP just as much as it does to other models. It is not about 'box ticking' – the forms which are suggested for recording the results of the RAMP methodology impose a certain amount of discipline and structure on the process, and would be required if RAMP were to become a suite of computer programs; however, the forms are *not* the key parts of the process, although record keeping in one way or another is very important. The key part of the RAMP process, without which it will certainly fail, is an inquiring, contemplative, sceptical human mind.

1.7 Why sponsored by civil engineers and actuaries?

As designers and project managers – and in many other roles – civil engineers have a significant involvement in major projects. At the root of their professional training is the application of engineering methodologies to forces and materials to create complex structural entities like bridges, large buildings, dams, power stations, and transport infrastructure. Awareness of risk is inherently incorporated into the discipline of civil engineering because the consequences of the failure of an engineering structure can potentially be catastrophic in terms of loss of life alone (as with the failure of a major dam). Until recently, however, civil engineers had only a limited exposure to some non-engineering financial risks – for example, inflation or the cost of capital – which are capable of having a major effect on the viability of projects. It is hoped that the RAMP methodology will encourage civil engineers to become more aware of the business side of projects and the way that a wider variety of risks can be managed. These considerations acquire added force with the revolution in procurement methods represented by the British Government's Private Finance Initiative (PFI).

Actuaries, on the other hand, are well versed in assessing a wide range of both technical and commercial risks, in evaluating investment portfolios and in the financial management of insurance companies and pension funds. In a totally different way, they are as aware as civil engineers of the need for effective identification and management of risks within their core disciplines, because most investors and investing institutions are for sound logical reasons risk averse (in the final analysis, aversion is the preferred attitude of most people towards risk). Traditionally the involvement of actuaries in major infrastructure projects has been slight because these were usually undertaken by a public sector that could (literally) afford to be almost totally unconcerned with financial risk which was underwritten by the taxpayer. This has changed with the PFI. Accordingly, the Faculty and Institute of Actuaries have together decided that the RAMP initiative is well worth pursuing as part of their current mission to take their profession into wider fields.

1.8 Who should use RAMP?

Although engineers and actuaries do have a strong interest in risk assessment and management, several other professions also have a legitimate involvement in the same field – notably, project managers, economists, management consultants, accountants, bankers, lawyers, fund managers, corporate finance professionals and public administrators. In fact, it is expected that RAMP will be of interest to anyone engaged in capital projects – whether as investors, decision-makers, consultants or managers.

The need for a comprehensive and systematic approach to risk management, such as RAMP, is highlighted by the increasing trend towards a broader packaging of risks – e.g. in finance-design-build-operate-maintain (FDBOM) concessions – and the transfer or sharing of risk for capital investments between public and private sectors (as under the PFI). These require an assessment at an early stage of all the risks throughout the investment life-cycle from initiation, during design and construction, through the operating period, to close-down of the investment. Furthermore, the parties involved often have difficulty in understanding risks outside their area of experience and may therefore overestimate them and not wish to understate them – e.g. contractors may be reluctant to take on operating franchises. It is expected that RAMP will make a significant contribution to the analysis, allocation and management of risks for such arrangements.

1.9 What benefits does it offer?

To summarise, it is intended that RAMP will

- assist in reducing risk exposures through better information and more effective management action
- lead to better decisions and give greater confidence to investors and other stakeholders
- highlight the roles of engineers and actuaries in risk analysis and management issues generally
- provide a valuable contribution to the wider community of professionals and managers engaged in projects
- enable better use to be made of the world's scarce resources by helping to prevent waste arising from failed projects.

1.10 PRAM

In December 1997 the Association for Project Management published a guide known as PRAM (Project Risk Analysis and Management), edited by Peter Simon, David Hillson and Ken Newland. It combines project managers' professional expertise into 'a practical and non-prescriptive process for the analysis and management of risk'.

We believe that the PRAM approach is basically consistent with the RAMP methodology. One of the key strengths of the PRAM guide is that it clearly describes a number of specialist techniques for risk identification, analysis and management, and shows how to put them into practice. It is therefore warmly recommended as useful reading for project managers and other experts, and rather less space is devoted here to these specialist topics than might otherwise have been the case.

In this publication describing RAMP methodology, we have concentrated more on the *strategic* aspects of risk appraisal and management, with particular reference to the financial implications. It is vitally important that the major risks involved in a project are properly evaluated and well understood by sponsors, lenders and investors as a basis for their decisions. We consider that the use of RAMP methodology will enable the risks to be minimised and any significant remaining risks to be properly identified, quantified and controlled, in the manner that these parties need.

At the same time, however, RAMP contains a wealth of ideas for practical application, including pointers to the wider use of insurance in future for risk reduction purposes. RAMP is not just a consistent theoretical framework, but a way of evaluating, minimising and controlling the risks in nearly all projects. The handbook shows with illustrative case studies how this methodology can be applied in order to optimise decision making at the strategic level.

1.11 Internet access

The Internet websites of the Faculty and Institute of Actuaries and the Institution of Civil Engineers have some pages on RAMP, including a simplified version of the RAMP process. The addresses of these websites are:

http://www.actuaries.org.uk
http://www.ice.org.uk

RAMP now also has its own website:
www.RAMPrisk.com

1.12 STRATRISK

As mentioned above, RAMP is a tool for the strategic appraisal of projects. The RAMP working party is now turning its attention to the wider aspects of strategic risk in existing businesses. It is hoped to construct a simple framework (currently known as STRATRISK), which will assist company boards and public-sector decision makers to focus on the vital strategic risks and uncertainties (both upside and downside) inherent in their business activities. RAMP itself will then be able to be viewed as an important tool within this overall framework.

Overview of RAMP

2.1 Basic concepts

The basic idea behind RAMP is extremely simple. It can be illustrated by considering the steps you take when considering going for a country walk with your family when on holiday. First you and your family agree the objectives for the walk. You *identify* the risks, such as being caught in a thunderstorm, encountering a muddy path or getting lost. You then *analyse* the likelihood of each such event and how serious the consequences might be, for example ruined clothing or getting back too late to go to the show for which you have tickets.

The next step is to identify the *risk mitigation options*, such as carrying umbrellas and rainwear, wearing boots, taking a map and compass, or taking a mobile phone to call a taxi if necessary. In each case there will be an inconvenience or cost factor and a decision will have to be made on whether mitigation is worthwhile.

Unless all the risks are mitigated, some *residual risks* will remain. Suppose it is decided not to take rainwear. The residual storm risk will then have to be *controlled* by keeping an eye on the sky and heading for shelter in time if black clouds roll up. The time risk will likewise have to be controlled by occasionally looking at a watch so that the taxi can be called when necessary. If we take the mobile phone, this will introduce a *secondary* risk, namely that it might be lost or stolen.

These concepts of setting the project objective, followed by the identification, analysis and mitigation of the risks, and control of the residual risks, lie at the heart of the RAMP process. For a major project the situation is much more complicated than a country walk, with far more risks and the probable introduction of numerous secondary risks arising from the mitigation actions selected. Some of the risks will be dependent on others and many of the probabilities, costs and outcomes will be uncertain.

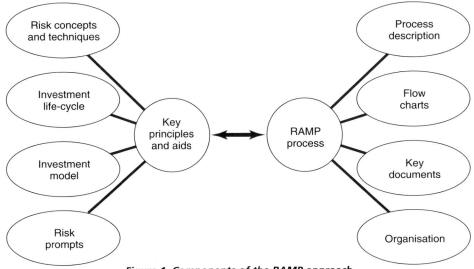

Figure 1. Components of the RAMP approach

2.2 Pre-requisites for RAMP

In order to understand and apply the RAMP approach the user needs a basic understanding of the following (see fig.1).

- *Key principles and aids:* covering some underlying concepts and techniques for risk analysis; a definition of the stages through which an investment progresses from start to finish; an investment model which relates the various costs and benefits arising from the investment to some overall measure of its value (e.g. its net present value); and risk prompts to assist in the identification and evaluation of risks.
- *RAMP process:* comprising a description of the process; supporting flow charts; details of the key documents created during each activity of the process; and the organisation to be adopted in order to apply RAMP.

Each component is outlined in turn below, starting with those on the left hand side of Fig. 1 (the key principles and aids), followed by those on the right hand side (the components of the RAMP process).

2.3 Risk concepts and techniques

For the purpose of RAMP, 'risk' can be defined as a threat (or opportunity) which could affect adversely (or favourably) achievement of the objectives of an investment. However, users of RAMP need to have an understanding of risk which extends beyond this simple, succinct definition. They need an appreciation of some basic concepts of risk and techniques for risk analysis. These are summarised in Appendix 1. It may be useful by way of introduction to set out a few of the main ideas about risk which are applied in the RAMP process.

Risk events

In any risk analysis, it is necessary to begin by identifying the *risk events* which, if they occurred, could affect the outcome of the project, for better or worse (e.g. the collapse of a tunnel during construction of an underground railway). Particular attention should be paid to the identification of those events which could have very serious adverse implications for the project, even if they seem unlikely to happen (such as the sinking of the *Titanic*). We refer to these as 'strategic risks'.

Unforeseen risks

It is also important to think hard about whether there are some possible outcomes which could normally not be foreseen, because they depend on an unusual combination of circumstances or a change in the underlying situation which has not been envisaged. An example is the possibility that new warships might have to be sold to other navies, instead of being brought into commission as intended. The consideration of such risks (as far as this may be possible) is very important indeed; simply because they are unknown, such risks are very easy to omit. One of the crucial tasks in the RAMP process is to strive to identify as many of these risks as possible, despite the undoubted difficulties, since experience shows that it is such risks which are often the most dangerous for the viability of a project.

Likelihood

The next step is to assess the *likelihood* of each risk event occurring; this means the chance (or 'risk') that it will occur. Thus a 20% likelihood means that there is a one in five chance that the risk event will happen. It is twice as likely to occur as it would be if there were only a 10% likelihood. An event which is unlikely to happen has a likelihood only slightly greater than zero, whereas an event which is almost certain to happen has a likelihood only slightly less than 100%. In effect, therefore, we have a continuous scale of measurement, ranging from 0% to 100%, to express the degree of likelihood that an event will happen.

Another way of looking at likelihood, which some readers may find helpful, is to imagine the project being repeated (if that were possible) a very large number of times. Then an event with a likelihood of 10% could be expected to occur in about 10% of the projects and an event with a likelihood of 20% in about 20% of the projects.

Often the occurrence or non-occurrence of a particular risk event will depend on the occurrence or non-occurrence of a number of underlying causes. Thus it is often more appropriate to concentrate the analysis of likelihood on underlying causes, rather than the risk event itself. For example, suppose the event under consideration is of a bridge collapsing during construction. Two possible independent underlying causes of such a collapse might be identified, i.e. a design fault (having, say, a 0.05% likelihood) or faulty assembly (having, say, a 0.10% likelihood). We can add the two probabilities together and say that the chance of the bridge collapsing is about 0.15%.

We have spoken as if we know for certain that a particular risk event has a fixed numerical chance of occurring. In practice, it is usually not known with absolute precision what the chance of occurrence actually is. All we have is a perception, based on opinion and research, which is probably not quite correct and may occasionally be wide of the mark. For example, the true chance of occurrence of an event which is assessed as having a likelihood of 20% might be, say, 25%. For this reason the sensitivity of calculations must be tested by varying the values assumed to see whether this makes much difference to the picture which emerges from the analysis.

This concept of sensitivity testing is of great importance in risk analysis. Whenever an

assumption is made or a value is estimated, the effect of using credible alternative assumptions or values must be evaluated and recorded. The results thus obtained will be useful in assessing the reliability of the overall analysis and may sometimes point to a greater range (or a more dispersed probability distribution) of possible outcomes for the project as a whole than is otherwise indicated.

Sometimes, of course, we may be well aware that we do not have nearly enough information to assess the likelihood with even a tolerable degree of accuracy. In other words, there is a high degree of uncertainty. We might know enough to be able to say that the likelihood probably lies within certain specified limits, but if this is a wide band for an event which would have significant consequences if it occurred, the result might well be that we are unable to make rational decisions about the future of the project. In such a situation it might be worth carrying out research to improve our knowledge and reduce the uncertainty. Suppose, for example, that the initial assessment is that an event which could have very serious adverse consequences has a likelihood which could be anywhere in the range of 0% to 25%. If the risk could not be eliminated, transferred or avoided, it is unlikely that the sponsor would proceed with the project. If, however, research was undertaken which showed that the true likelihood was around 1%, many sponsors would be prepared to accept this comparatively low risk and go ahead. Uncertainty is often more difficult to analyse and 'manage' than risk, although the downside possibilities associated with uncertainty can often be mitigated to some extent, despite the lack of accurate knowledge.

Impact

Up to this point we have been concerned only with the chance or likelihood that a particular event occurs. However, we also need to consider the possible consequences if it occurs, e.g. a delay, and in particular the financial consequences, which we call the *impact*. Clearly, it is important to do this, since a 5% likelihood of losing £1 000 000 is much more serious than a 5% likelihood of losing only £1000. Sensitivity testing is important here too.

Expected value

We can obtain a good measure of the financial value or cost to be placed on different risks by multiplying the likelihood by the impact, to give the *expected value*. Thus a 5% likelihood of losing £1 000 000 would have an expected value of £50 000. A 5% likelihood of losing £1000 would have an expected value of £50.

One way of looking at the expected value is that it is equivalent to the insurance premium which one would have to pay an insurance company in order to cover the risk (ignoring the loadings which the insurance company would apply in practice for expenses, profit, etc.). Thus the premium would have to be £50 000 to cover a 5% risk of losing £1 000 000. This is because if there were a large number of such risks being covered by the insurance company, the total of the premiums would then exactly equal the sums paid out in claims for the events which occur. The expected value is therefore a good measure of the true financial value of the risk, taking into account both the likelihood that the event will occur and the impact if it does.

Often, however, an event (if it occurs) will not have a single unique impact. There may be a range of possible impacts, each with a different probability. In such cases it may be appropriate to derive the expected value of the risk by using the average impact, obtained by weighting each of the possible impacts by its own probability.

The four concepts we have mentioned of *risk event, likelihood, impact* and *expected value* lie right at the heart of RAMP. They enable us to place a realistic financial value on each risk, depending on

how likely the event in question is to occur and what would be the impact if it did. Once we have attached such financial values to risks, we can rank them in order of importance and we can also form a preliminary idea of how much it is worth spending in order to mitigate them. For example, it would not normally be worth spending £20 000 in order to mitigate a non-catastrophic risk which has an expected value of only £1000.

However, it would be dangerous if decision-makers were to look only at expected values when deciding on whether to proceed with a project. This is because expected values conceal some of the more extreme possible outcomes. For example, if there is a chance of 0.1% that an event will occur costing £10 000 000, the expected value of this risk will be only £10 000. If one were only considering expected values, this risk would seem less important than another risk having an expected value of £30 000, based on a 40% likelihood of an event having an impact of £75 000.

Nevertheless, the occurrence of the first of the two risk events mentioned above could cripple or bankrupt the sponsor. Hence the sponsor will often wish to pay particular attention to the existence of such a risk and seek to mitigate it as far as possible, even if the cost of doing so exceeds the expected value.

Probability distribution

For the same reason it is important to show decision-makers the full range of possible financial outcomes for the project as a whole (taking account of all the risks to which it is subject) and the degree of likelihood which can be attached to each outcome. This is called a *probability distribution* of possible outcomes, and is the fifth key concept of RAMP. The decision-maker will use it as a basis for deciding whether the degree of downside risk is acceptable or not. In doing so he or she will exercise judgement, bearing in mind the extent to which the sponsor could afford to bear the more unfavourable outcomes, should they occur, and the likelihood that such outcomes will happen. The decision-maker will also take into account the possible upside outcomes and their likelihood.

Using judgement

The risk analyst must be able to think very clearly in order to distinguish between the various types of risk, combine them correctly with due allowance for mutual dependency where relevant, and avoid falling into the many traps which exist for the unwary. It is not a matter of carrying out mechanical analysis, but of keeping a clear head and a questioning frame of mind. Risk specialists are trained and experienced in such work, and it will usually be worthwhile to employ them from the

outset (possibly using an external consultancy firm) to avoid unwise decisions or disappointments when lenders or investors refuse to proceed because the risks are too high.

2.4 Investment life-cycle

The investment life-cycle is a description of the successive stages through which an investment progresses from start to finish. It defines the overall framework within which RAMP is carried out. The version of the investment life-cycle adopted for RAMP has six separate but sometimes overlapping stages as described below.

- *Opportunity identification:* in which the potential investment is identified, and an initial assessment is made to decide whether to proceed with a full appraisal.
- *Appraisal:* which involves determining the investment objectives, scope and requirements; defining the project structure and strategy; developing the business case; identifying funding options; identifying, analysing and deciding how to mitigate the risks; and conducting a feasibility study prior to deciding whether to make the investment.
- *Investment planning:* comprising the procurement of funding; obtaining of planning consents; undertaking preliminary design work; planning project implementation; preparing a detailed risk mitigation plan; and making a final decision to proceed with the investment.
- *Asset creation:* including planning, designing, procuring, constructing and commissioning the asset. (This stage is sometimes referred to as 'the project' but in this handbook we use the word 'project' to mean the activities occuring during the whole life-cycle of the investment.)
- *Operation:* using the asset to provide a service so as to derive revenue and other benefits, while maintaining and renewing the asset.

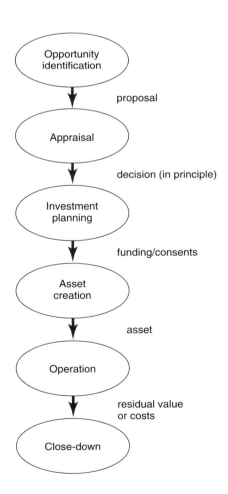

Figure 2. Investment life-cycle

Table 1. Activities, key parameters and RAMP process in each stage of investment life-cycle

Investment stage/ Objective	Principal activities	Key parameters	RAMP process
Opportunity identification To identify opportunity and decide whether it is worthwhile conducting a full appraisal	Identify business need Define investment opportunity Make initial assessment Decide whether to proceed with appraisal	Broad estimate of capital cost and cash flows Cost appraisal	Preliminary review
Appraisal To decide whether the investment should be made	Define investment objectives, scope and requirements Define project structure and strategy Develop business case Identify funding options Conduct feasibility study Decide (in principle) whether to proceed with investment	Refined estimates of capital cost and cash flows Cost of investment planning phase	Full risk review
Investment planning To prepare for effective implementation of the project	Procurement of funding Obtaining planning consents Preliminary design work Compiling project implementation plan Placing advance contracts (e.g. site preparation) Making final decision to proceed with investment	Financing cost Refined estimates of capital cost and cash flows	Risk review (prior to final decision)
Asset creation To design, construct and commission the asset, and prepare for operation	Mobilising the project team Detailed planning and design Procurement/tendering Construction Testing, commissioning and hand-over Ensuring safety Preparing for operation	Project objectives: - scope* - performance/quality* - timing* - capital cost	Risk reviews (during or towards end of each activity) and risk management between risk reviews
Operation To operate the asset to obtain optimum benefits for client and other principal stakeholders (including investors and customers)	Operating the service Deriving revenue and other benefits Maintaining and renewing the asset	Operating cost Maintenance cost Cost of renewals Revenue Non-revenue benefits	Risk reviews (periodically)
Close-down To complete investment, dispose of asset and related business, and review its success	Sale, transfer, decommissioning or termination of asset and related business Post-investment review	Decommissioning cost Cost of staff redundancies Disposal cost Resale or residual value	Final risk review and RAMP close-down

* These have a potential impact on one or more financial parameters

- *Close-down:* which refers to the end of the investment life-cycle, when the franchise or concession period ends, or when the asset is sold or reaches the end of its economic life and is decommissioned.

The six stages of the investment life-cycle, and the main end results from each stage, are shown in Fig. 2.

The above stages may, of course, be varied in practice to meet the requirements of a particular situation.

The RAMP approach aims to identify, evaluate and manage the risks which could cause the project to vary from the most likely or expected outcome. Table 1 shows the main objectives, activities, associated parameters, and the risk management processes in each stage of the investment life-cycle.

Three key management roles need to be performed in carrying out the successive stages of a capital investment: the client, project manager and operator. The client is, or acts for, the project owner and is therefore accountable for the overall investment. The project manager is accountable to the client for the planning and execution of the work to create the asset needed to achieve the objectives of the investment. The operator is responsible for using the asset to provide the benefits expected from the investment. Although the client has overall responsibility, all three roles need to be involved at various stages of the investment life-cycle.

The client is most directly and actively concerned in the first three stages, which involve defining, developing and justifying the investment and obtaining funding and planning consents. Typically, a development manager will be delegated responsibility for managing these early stages. The project

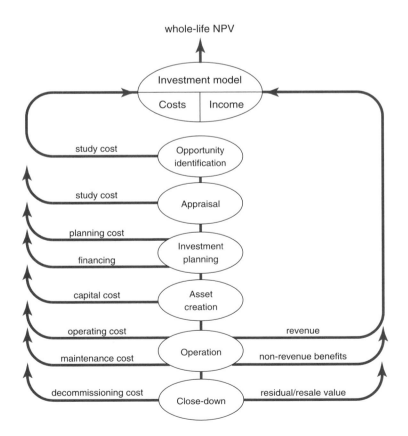

Figure 3. Investment model

manager directs the fourth stage to create the asset. The operator has primary responsibility for operating the asset and generating benefits (in the fifth stage). All three roles may be involved in the sixth and final stage, close-down, the leading role depending on the situation and nature of close-down.

2.5 Investment model

A way is needed for evaluating financially the risks to which an investment is exposed in terms of the objectives and the parameters used to define them (e.g. revenue, other benefits, capital and operating costs). Also needed is some overall measure of the value of the investment (e.g. pay-back, IRR or whole-life NPV). A suitable investment model needs to be developed in order to

- estimate the likely financial outcome of the project and ascertain whether it meets any predetermined financial criteria as to what constitutes a viable project
- estimate the extent to which the financial outcome may vary from the likely value, and the probabilities of different degrees of variation
- show which methods of risk mitigation are financially worthwhile.

An appropriate structure for such a model is illustrated in Fig. 3. Details of how the model can be constructed and used in conjunction with RAMP are set out in Appendix 2. The key parameters are gross revenues, the value of any other benefits, capital costs and operating costs.

For preliminary appraisals a simple investment model can often be processed by hand with the aid of no more than a pocket calculator. For a full appraisal it would be more typical for the investment model to be set out in the form of a spreadsheet which is processed by computer. Where, as is often the case for major projects, the main aim of the investment model is to calculate the net present value (NPV) of the project, each parameter in the financial model is represented by a single value or a series of cash flows. Each of these is then converted into an NPV using an appropriate discount rate, so that the estimated whole-life NPV for the project can be calculated. During the RAMP process, the financial model is used repeatedly to assess how potential impacts of risks on the individual parameters affect the whole-life NPV of the investment – i.e. the 'riskiness' of the investment. This is typically done by using scenario analyses, Monte Carlo simulation or sensitivity analysis. A similar method can be used to compute the internal rate of return (IRR) where this is required.

2.6 Risk prompts

One of the main tasks in RAMP is to identify risks as comprehensively as possible. A risk which has not even been identified cannot be analysed or evaluated, let alone mitigated. Hence, it is of great importance to do everything possible to list every risk to which the project in question could be exposed. Brainstorming sessions and desk studies are very useful for this purpose but in addition it is often helpful to use risk prompts, which suggest possible areas of risk, to uncover further risks which may affect the project. Examples of risk prompts are checklists, risk maps and risk matrices. Appendix 3 sets out a comprehensive risk matrix and Appendix 1 (page 60) gives a checklist of unexpected risks.

2.7 Process description

The RAMP process consists of four *activities,* which are generally carried out at different times in the life-cycle of an investment as indicated below.

- *Process launch:* conducted early in the investment life-cycle.
- *Risk review:* conducted before key decisions or at intervals.

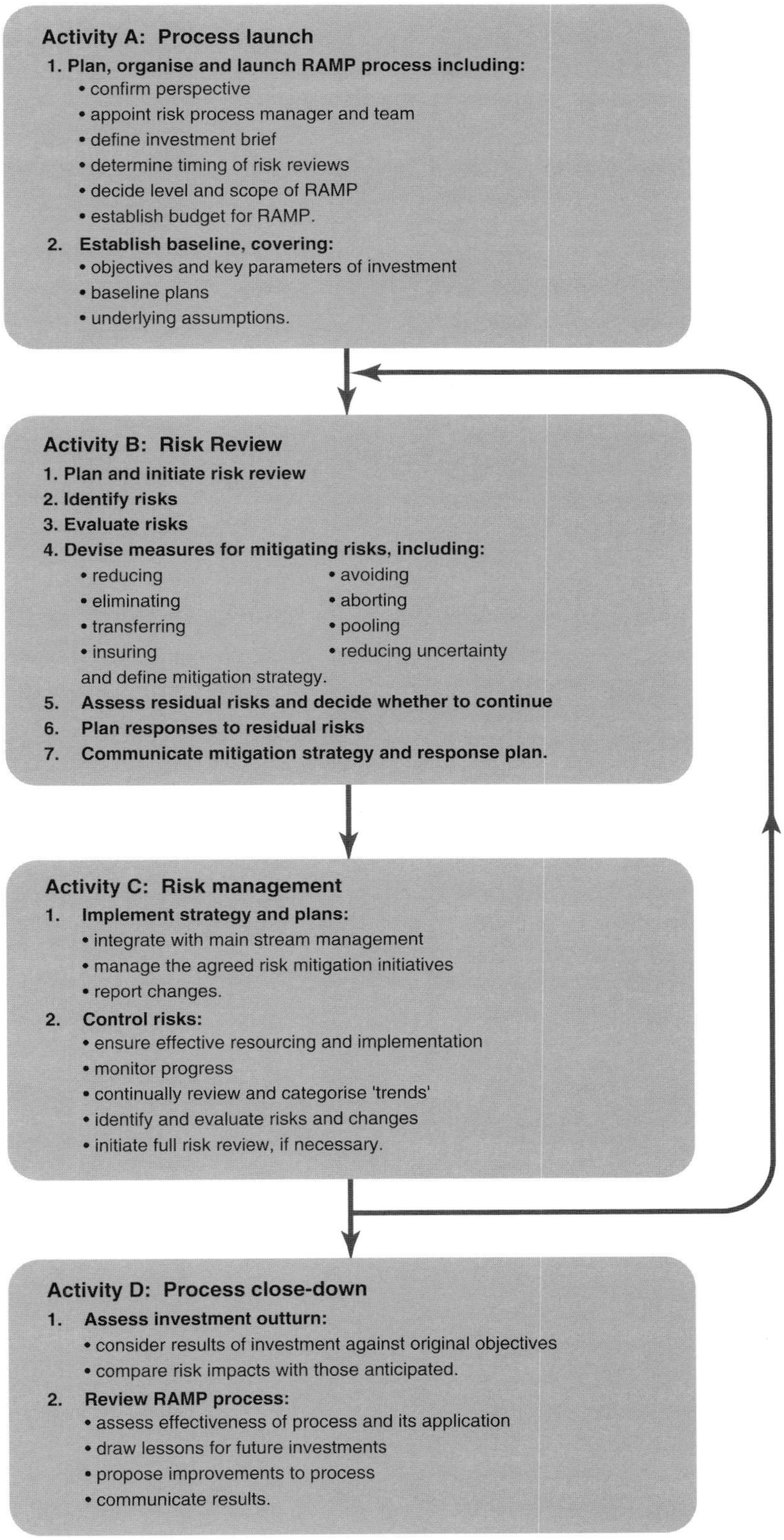

Activity A: Process launch

1. **Plan, organise and launch RAMP process including:**
   - confirm perspective
   - appoint risk process manager and team
   - define investment brief
   - determine timing of risk reviews
   - decide level and scope of RAMP
   - establish budget for RAMP.
2. **Establish baseline, covering:**
   - objectives and key parameters of investment
   - baseline plans
   - underlying assumptions.

Activity B: Risk Review

1. **Plan and initiate risk review**
2. **Identify risks**
3. **Evaluate risks**
4. **Devise measures for mitigating risks, including:**
   - reducing
   - eliminating
   - transferring
   - insuring

   - avoiding
   - aborting
   - pooling
   - reducing uncertainty

   and define mitigation strategy.
5. **Assess residual risks and decide whether to continue**
6. **Plan responses to residual risks**
7. **Communicate mitigation strategy and response plan.**

Activity C: Risk management

1. **Implement strategy and plans:**
   - integrate with main stream management
   - manage the agreed risk mitigation initiatives
   - report changes.
2. **Control risks:**
   - ensure effective resourcing and implementation
   - monitor progress
   - continually review and categorise 'trends'
   - identify and evaluate risks and changes
   - initiate full risk review, if necessary.

Activity D: Process close-down

1. **Assess investment outturn:**
   - consider results of investment against original objectives
   - compare risk impacts with those anticipated.
2. **Review RAMP process:**
   - assess effectiveness of process and its application
   - draw lessons for future investments
   - propose improvements to process
   - communicate results.

Figure 4. RAMP process

- *Risk management*: conducted continually between risk reviews.
- *Process close-down:* conducted at the end of the investment life-cycle or on premature termination.

Each activity is composed of several *phases*, each of which is made up of a number of process *steps.* The first and last activities – process launch and process close-down – are each performed once only, around the start and end of the investment. There are a number of risk reviews carried out at crucial stages or time intervals within the investment life-cycle. Risk management activities are performed continually between risk reviews based on the analyses, strategies and plans produced by the preceding risk review. The process launch will normally be part of (or shortly followed by) the first risk review, and the process close-down will be part of (or shortly follow) the final risk review.

Although the process launch is generally undertaken in full only once early in the life of the investment, it is likely to be necessary to reconsider and revise its results and objectives during subsequent risk reviews and risk

management activities – e.g. to reflect changes in investment objectives or other circumstances, possibly arising in response to risk analyses.

Successive risk reviews and risk management activities will change in scope and focus as the investment progresses through the various stages in its life-cycle. At each review, risks whose exposures have ended will be eliminated from the analyses and plans, and their contingency provisions released; otherwise, each review will focus on future risks, in the remaining stages of the investment (and not just the risks in the current stage).

Risk management does not end with the construction of a project. Often the revenue risk – the risk that the net revenue stream may differ substantially from that which has been predicted – has a great impact on the viability of the project and will therefore require more careful and continuing analysis than risks which would have a lower financial impact if they occurred.

The RAMP process is outlined in Fig. 4, and discussed in greater detail in Chapters 3 to 8. Appendix 9 sets out the process formally for ease of reference.

Table 2. Key documents covering the four activities of RAMP

Activity	Key document
Activity A: Process launch	RAMP process plan Risk diary (used in each activity)
Activity B: Risk review	Risk review plan Risk register (including residual risk analysis) Risk mitigation strategy Risk response plan Investment model runs Risk review report
Activity C: Risk management	Trend schedules
Activity D: Process close-down	RAMP close-down report

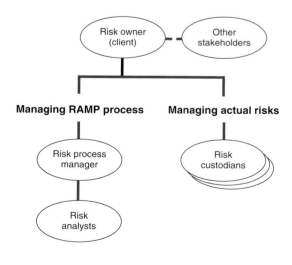

Figure 5. Organising for RAMP

2.8 Flowcharts

The process is illustrated diagramatically in the form of flowcharts in Appendix 10. These indicate the iterative nature of RAMP.

2.9 Key documents

As explained above, RAMP involves completing a number of key documents to record the analyses, plans and other results from the process as it progresses. The ten key documents used to cover the four activities of RAMP are listed in Table 2.

A table describing the purpose, contents and uses of each of the key documents is given in Appendix 11. It is assumed that users will prefer to devise their own document formats.

2.10 Organisation

Every aspect of the investment cycle is exposed to some risk, therefore many people will be involved in some facets of risk analysis and management. To undertake this effectively an appropriate organisational framework with a clear assignment of roles and responsibilities needs to be established.

As shown in Fig. 5 there are two main aspects of managing risks using RAMP.

- *Managing the RAMP process:* i.e. planning, implementing and supervising the process for risk analysis and management.
- *Managing actual risks:* i.e. deciding what mitigation measures to adopt, and taking appropriate actions to respond to and control risks.

RAMP normally deals with risk from the perspective of the owner/client, who is the *risk owner* or acts for one or more investors or other *stakeholders* involved. There may be several other stakeholders, each with different perspectives and

risk exposures, for example

- bank or funding agency
- central or local government
- developer
- other revenue generators (e.g. retailers, car park operators and advertisers)
- franchisees, concessionaires and contractors
- customers and the public at large.

The owner/client needs to be aware of the stakeholders and of their respective interests, and take these into account when considering how best to deal with each risk. Some of the other parties may be willing to accept risks at a lower price than the owner's estimate of likely cost. In fact one party's risk can be another party's opportunity. For example, a serious fire in a new hotel nearing completion could cause the owner serious delays and loss of potential business, but result in profitable further work for the contractor.

It would be possible for RAMP to be applied from the viewpoint of one of the stakeholders other than the owner/client, in which case some suitable modifications would need to be made to the organisational structure described below. In practice, however, it might sometimes be possible for the owner/client to share its own RAMP analysis with other interested stakeholders so that only a minimum of extra work is required in order to focus the analysis on the stakeholder's own objectives and risk profiles.

As a general principle, a particular type of risk should be the responsibility of the party who

- has the greatest understanding and competence in dealing with it
- has access to the most information about the incidence, timing and impact of the risk
- is best able to control it.

A crucial principle of RAMP is that a single named individual should be assigned to control each principal area of risk on behalf of the owner/client during implementation of the project. These are the *risk custodians*. They will usually be senior executives engaged in the mainstream management of the investment who are made accountable on behalf of the owner/client for managing risks within their designated areas of responsibility – typically, the client's development director in the early stages, the project manager in the asset creation stage and the operator for the operating stage. However, additional or different risk custodians may be appointed to manage particular categories of risks, such as threats to planning consents, political risks, financing problems or competitors' actions. The risk custodians are required to review regularly all significant risk exposures and impacts, suggest appropriate mitigation measures, and respond to residual risks within their assigned areas, keeping the risk process manager up to date with developments.

To initiate and manage the RAMP process it is necessary to appoint a *risk process manager*, who will

- plan and launch the RAMP process
- lead individual risk reviews
- ensure that the risk analysts (if more than one),

who carry out the project appraisal cover the whole field of potential risks between them without any gaps

- co-ordinate and monitor risk management measures
- report on progress in risk management
- draw lessons from experience in using RAMP to improve future RAMP initiatives within the organisation.

The risk process manager – ideally someone who is not performing other roles for the investment – should be appointed at an early stage in the life of the investment so as to ensure effective and consistent application of the RAMP process from the outset. Depending on the size and complexity of the investment, the risk process manager could be full or part time, and possibly an external consultant.

2.11 Simplified version of RAMP

A simplified version of RAMP can be applied for the preliminary analysis of a project or for the full analysis of a smaller project. Details are set out in Appendix 7.

Launching the RAMP process

3.1 Defining the RAMP strategy

This chapter is the first part of the description of the RAMP process, which is continued in Chapters 4 to 8 and set out more formally in Appendix 9. The first task is to confirm the perspective from which the risk analysis and management is being carried out and identify the principal stakeholders interested in the outcome. This version of the RAMP process assumes that risk is being considered from the viewpoint of the owner (i.e. the party which makes and owns the investment). The process can be adapted to suit other interests. Other stakeholders could typically include major shareholders, joint venture partners, the government, bankers, insurers and contractors.

A risk process manager will be appointed, who will plan, lead and co-ordinate the risk analysis and management process, and report on its results (see Section 2.10). In addition, the risk process manager's reporting line will need to be established to ensure firm accountability. His or her initial task will be to prepare a *RAMP process plan* which deals with all the matters in this chapter.

A preliminary brief on the objectives, scope and timing of the investment, including an assessment of its value and importance to the sponsoring organisation, and its complexity, should be prepared at this stage. This should include the definition of the provisional overall strategy for risk reviews and management throughout the investment life-cycle, including each of the following.

- *Purpose of RAMP:* what are the objectives of the RAMP process as applied to this investment (e.g. what key decisions or actions will depend on the results)?
- *Level of risk analysis:* what level of detail, sophistication and effort is appropriate for such

an investment/project, given its type, value, complexity and importance?
- *Scope of review:* what stages in the investment life-cycle, or more specific aspects of the investment, are to be considered (if a comprehensive approach is not required)?
- *Stage/timing:* at what points or times within each stage are the risk reviews to be carried out?
- *Budget for RAMP:* establish a budget for conducting the RAMP process stage-by-stage for the life of the investment – or at least for the early stages.

It is essential that the risk analysis and management strategy is communicated as fully as possible to all concerned. The involvement of as many people as possible will make it more effective.

Next a RAMP process team will be formed by identifying and assigning those who will act as *risk analysts* to identify risks, help to evaluate them and devise suitable responses. Depending on the level of RAMP analysis intended, there may be one or a number of people required to act as risk analysts. Ideally, the most appropriate key executives or specialists within the organisation, and appropriately qualified and experienced external experts, should be assigned the task of identifying risks for each stage of the investment life-cycle or principal activity within a stage.

The risk process manager should introduce and maintain throughout the RAMP process a *risk diary* in which to note:
- significant events in planning and executing the RAMP process
- problems encountered
- perceptions about major unresolved uncertainties

- valuable contributions towards the success of the investment or the review
- major results of the review (by cross-referencing any other documents produced)
- unforeseen risks which arise
- ideas for improving the review and its management.

3.2 Establishing the baseline

The baseline consists of the objectives, and the underlying assumptions, information and plans which underpin the evaluation of project risk and its subsequent management. This involves determining the information outlined below. The level of detail at this stage depends on the scale and complexity of the investment, but each item in the following list should be covered.

- *Investment definition:* what are the aims, scope and timing of the investment?
- *Objectives:* what are the specific objectives and key 'deliverables' of the investment? The objectives need the most careful consideration and definition right at the outset; they will often be more extensive than appears at first sight. A failure to define the objectives fully may well result in a failure to identify the risks properly.
- *Key parameters:* what are the financial and other parameters which define or affect the objectives in each stage of the investment life-cycle? Examples include: values over time of capital cost, revenue, operating and maintenance costs. These values should include effects on other investments/projects and other company operations.
- *Overall measure (or measures) of investment:* in this description of the process the overall measure is assumed to be whole-life NPV, but there are numerous alternative measures which may be considered more suitable in some

situations, including: IRR, payback period, annualised rate of return, cost/benefit ratio. 'Real option techniques' may also sometimes be applicable.

- *Investment life-cycle:* what are the stages and sub-stages in the investment life-cycle?
- *Principal activities:* what are the main, separate activities in each stage of the life-cycle, how are they related, and how do they impact on each parameter and 'deliverable'?
- *Asset components and factors:* what are the major components of the asset to be created, what are the principal factors affecting the project, internally and externally, and how are these related?
- *Baseline plans:* what are the investment strategy, organisational framework, master programme, funding arrangements and business plan for carrying forward the investment?
- *Underlying assumptions:* what are the main assumptions on which the investment/project objectives, strategy and plans are based? These should be listed in an assumptions list in which additional entries will be made as the work progresses.
- *Investment model:* what is the financial model which defines how the key investment parameters interrelate and impact on the overall measure of value for the investment? The model should include allowances for the impact of the investment on other investments and operations of the organisation. It should also (where appropriate) take account of the magnitude and timing of the effects of inflation, taxation and currency fluctuations.
- *Discount rate:* what should be the discount rate used to assess the NPV? Generally, the higher the unquantifiable level of risks, the higher the discount rate should be.

- *Initial values and cash flows:* what are the values and cash flows assumed for each key parameter associated with each activity in each stage of the investment?
- *Initial overall value(s):* using the investment model with the initial values and most likely cash flows, compute the initial whole-life NPV and undertake a sensitivity analysis to derive the variability in its value which could result from potential changes in the values of the individual parameters.

3.3 Reviewing the process launch

Although the process launch is generally undertaken in full only once, early in the life of the investment, it is likely to be necessary to reconsider and revise its results and objectives during subsequent risk reviews – for example, to reflect changes in investment objectives or other circumstances. It will also be a useful reference point after the project has finished, when the RAMP close-down report in written.

Starting the risk review

Chapters 4 to 8 show how RAMP is implemented stage by stage. This chapter explains how the risk review – the process for systematically identifying and evaluating risks – is carried out. Chapter 5 shows how risks can be mitigated while Chapters 6 and 7 explain how risks which cannot be eliminated may be managed. What happens when the project comes to an end is shown in Chapter 8.

Risk reviews will be performed at crucial stages or time intervals in the investment life-cycle. The process activity for the first full review is described below. Subsequent risk reviews will revise and update the analysis and resultant actions as appropriate at the time of the review.

4.1 Planning and initiating the risk review

The risk process manager and the risk review team should be confirmed (or appointed) for this review. The purpose, scope and level of the risk review will need to be decided. This involves determining the following.

- *Specific aims of this risk review:* how are results of the risk analysis and responses to be used (e.g. what key decisions or actions will depend on them)?
- *Scope of review:* what stages or aspects of the investment are to be considered (if a comprehensive review is not required)?
- *Stage:* what is the stage reached in the investment/project life-cycle when the review is being performed?
- *Level of risk analysis:* what degree of detail, sophistication and effort is appropriate?

The next step is to plan the review by

- compiling an action plan
- defining resource requirements
- establishing a budget and timetable.

The above information, together with the aims, scope and level of analysis and the staffing and organisation for the risk review, comprise the *risk review plan*. All of the other parties likely to be involved in the review should be briefed about its purpose and timetable and the identities (names and roles) of those who will be participating in the review.

4.2 Identification of risks

The aims of this phase of RAMP are to

- identify, as exhaustively as practicable, all significant types and sources of risk and uncertainty associated with each of the investment objectives and the key parameters relating to these objectives
- ascertain the causes of each risk
- assess how risks are related to other risks and how risks should be classified and grouped for evaluation.

This is clearly a crucial phase. If a risk is not identified it cannot be evaluated and managed. The process of searching for and responding to risks is iterative. First each risk analyst attempts to list the risks associated with each objective, key parameter, major 'deliverable' or principal activity within that risk analyst's area of focus. It is essential that every relevant aspect of the investment is analysed by the team of risk analysts. The first attempt should be from first principles without the use of any checklist or other prompts, to avoid constraining the process of discovery. The resulting risks are listed in the risk register.

After this the risk analysts should repeat the exercise with the help of the risk matrix (Appendix 3) and other prompt aids such as

- check-lists of problems from: previous similar investments and projects, other case studies, technical papers, safety reviews and environmental impact studies
- site visits
- review of baseline plans, other key documents and outline designs.

Resulting risks should then be listed in the risk register for subsequent review and analysis, with a tentative indication of the significance of each risk ('clearly significant', 'possibly significant' and 'probably insignificant') and inter-relationships between risks. 'Significant' is to be interpreted as implying a risk the potential consequence of which could have a significant effect on one of the objectives, parameters or 'deliverables', even if it has only a small probability of occurrence. At this stage, no risks should be eliminated or ignored, because even seemingly minor risks can combine to have a major impact.

Some or all of the risk analysts, and others who can make a valuable contribution, are next brought together for a brainstorming session to review the risks previously identified and to flush out further risks. Brainstorming should be in two parts. The first starts from scratch without any indications of the risks identified by the risk analysts. The second starts with the risks listed in part one and those listed by the risk analysts, and attempts to find additional risk exposure with the aid of a risk matrix and any other appropriate prompt lists. Participants should be encouraged to mention even seemingly unlikely risks and scenarios. The risk register is extended and revised in the light of the results of the brainstorming.

It may be appropriate to interview or commission experts in particular aspects of the investment to identify risks which might otherwise be overlooked or not understood. It might also be useful to search relevant literature describing case studies of similar investments at home and overseas to learn about the risks encountered and the mitigation measures and responses adopted. Again, any resulting risks are entered in the risk register.

Having identified as many risks as practicable in this phase of the review, it is necessary to classify and if appropriate group risks to assist in their evaluation. This is done by considering each risk in the risk register in turn to determine and record

- possible cause or causes of the risk
- trigger events giving rise to risk occurring
- possible timing and potential frequency of occurrence
- range of possible consequences – both physical and financial
- asset component, factor or activity associated with the risk
- objective, 'deliverable' or parameter impacted
- other related risks
- form of relationship with other risks (e.g. common causes, one risk depending on occurrence of others, timing sequence of risks or causes or activities to which the risks relate)
- who currently owns the risk (e.g. the party who controls or is directly affected by it)
- the initial responses to the risk (e.g. what would be the first ideas on how to mitigate or respond to the risk – it may not be the most effective response but later analysis will discover that)
- whether there are any risks which should be eliminated because they duplicate or overlap with each other.

The analysis and understanding of risk groupings and relationships is often aided by representing them in the form of precedence, influence, risk/response or other diagrams, which should be appended to the risk register with suitable cross-references. Any new assumptions identified at this stage should be entered into the assumptions list.

4.3 Evaluation of risks

For each identified risk which has a 'clearly significant' or 'possibly significant' consequence if it occurs, it may be convenient to assess in the first instance qualitatively and approximately the values described below.

- The likelihood/frequency of the risk occurring per unit of time or some other convenient unit (i.e. will it occur once in every week, month, year, 10 years, 100 years, etc.). We describe below some ways of expressing likelihood.
- The potential consequence (with respect to one or more of the parameters or related cash flows) if the risk occurs.
- The most likely frequency of the risk occurring during the whole lifetime of the investment.
- The likely timing of the risk's impact
- The acceptance score, by combining the likelihood with the consequence, using the risk assessment tables (Tables 15 to 17) in Appendix 4. The use of risk assessment tables is often a helpful aid to the prioritisation of risks, although it is not an essential step in the RAMP process. The tables give each risk event a 'score', according to how likely it is to occur and how serious an impact it would have if it occurred, and the risks with the highest scores are the more serious ones selected for initial evaluation in greater depth. The reason for this prioritisation is that, if the more serious risks prove incapable of being sufficiently mitigated, then the whole future of the project may be in doubt and it may not be worth analysing the less serious risks.

The likelihood (or probability) of a risk event may be expressed in several ways:

- a once and for all chance of occurrence
- an average rate of occurrence over the duration of the investment
- a variable rate of occurrence
- a physical extent of occurrence (e.g. per kilometre of rail track)
- a probability of each of a series of possible values or ranges of values over the life of the investment (i.e. a probability distribution).

It is important to start with a natural or convenient basis for estimation, and link this to a life-cycle estimate. If there is a range of possible values, it may be acceptable, provided the range is not too wide, to represent the range by its mid point or average value. If this is not satisfactory a range of values may be quoted, e.g. likelihood between 0.2 and 0.4, and consequence between £1 million and £1.5 million, and hence expected value between £0.2 million and £0.6 million.

If a risk is related to one or more other risks – in the sense that they share common causes or for other reasons the occurrence of one affects the likelihood of another – the related risks should be evaluated together. If the risks are not related, i.e. are independent, they can be evaluated separately. The resulting assessment of each risk or group of related risks should be entered in the risk register.

The risks that the assumptions set out in the assumptions list may not come true should be considered and evaluated in the same way as for other risks.

The significance of risks should be reviewed and then they should be reclassified into the categories of significance. For risks which are 'probably insignificant', the decision must be made as to whether they can be ignored, covered within a general risk category or retained in the analysis. Examples of general risk categories are an overall allowance for possible causes of cost increases due to 'design development', 'commercial environment at time of tendering', etc. As a general rule, risks should not be ignored unless there is absolute confidence that they are trivial.

Particular attention and care must be taken with identifying and classifying risks which could have either

- serious or catastrophic consequences or high expected values, or
- exceptionally favourable consequences.

All the risks in both of these categories are likely to need particular, individual attention when assessing the overall 'riskiness' of the investment.

A decision must be made about which risks justify and are amenable to more detailed evaluation and quantification. Generally, these are the risks with largest expected values or, if probabilities are low, with most serious consequences. In choosing the risks for further analysis, it will be necessary to ensure that the likely benefit accruing from refining the estimate is worth the effort and cost involved. However, this does not apply to risks with catastrophic consequences (even if the probability of occurrence is low) as these are nearly always worth further study. For each such risk, a more detailed and quantified evaluation of likelihood, consequence, timing, expected value and dependencies must be conducted, noting carefully any assumptions made.

A recommended method of doing this is that described by Chapman (1996) as the Simple Scenario approach, which develops subjectively a range of possible consequences and the associated probabilities. This applies a standard procedure to help suitably well-informed executives or experts to develop such a probability distribution systematically while minimising the tendency towards 'anchoring' and bias in the estimates. There are also other methods of scenario analysis, for example that used

in Appendix 8. In addition, there are more sophisticated techniques which may be used where a more rigorous approach is justified (e.g. the Monte Carlo technique).

For each activity affecting each parameter of the investment, the RAMP team should compile an estimate of the potential impact of unexpected risks over the phases of the investment life-cycle, based on experience and the complexity and uncertainties associated with the activity and parameter. It may be appropriate to do this by identifying general categories of risks and making a contingency allowance for each based on previous experience in similar investments. The results should be entered in the risk register.

Using an investment model (Appendix 2) and parameter estimates, the overall impact of risks on the whole-life net present value (NPV) of the investment (looking at both the range and dispersion of the simulated NPVs and the weighted average 'expected' NPV) should be determined. This may be achieved by calculating the NPV for each possible combination of risk impacts (i.e. all scenarios considered for the purpose of the analysis) or by producing a statistical distribution of the NPV using a computer-based Monte Carlo simulation, with different results depending on the assumptions used. Either way the result will be a probability distribution of the project's NPVs, showing the likelihood that each of the calculated NPVs will occur. Generally, the larger the potential financial outcome, the more serious the potential consequences of volatility in the estimated NPV, and therefore the more important it is to attempt to reduce the downside volatility, even though this is likely to be at the expense of a reduction in the expected NPV.

Since these calculations are based on no more than a series of estimated parameters, it is important to test the sensitivity of the calculations by substituting alternative values of the key parameters, including other plausible figures for the likelihood and impact of the principal risk events. This gives an idea of the degree of confidence one can have in the calculated probability distribution of NPVs and indicates the extent of the possible variation. Assumptions that various risks are independent or dependent may also be tested within this framework.

In calculating the NPV, it will often be appropriate to make a downward adjustment to allow for the likelihood of reduced revenues at certain times in the future on account of cyclical economic downturns.

A preliminary assessment will then be made of the extent to which the major risks can be mitigated – i.e. reduced, eliminated, transferred, avoided, absorbed or pooled – and the results will be recorded in the risk register. Details of the methodology are given in Chapter 5. The aim at

this preliminary mitigation planning stage, however, will be limited to establishing whether optional courses of action exist which, on the face of it, may reduce the major risks to acceptable levels. If, in the case of a major risk, such options cannot be identified, consideration should be given at this stage to whether the project should be aborted or substantially modified.

An overall preliminary judgement should also be made as to whether the project looks like being sufficiently profitable to justify further analysis, having regard to the expected value of the NPV (after making a crude adjustment for the cost of the main mitigation options), the degree of confidence one can put in it, and other factors.

Assuming that there are good prospects for mitigating the major risks and that the project still appears likely to be profitable, the next stage is to proceed with planning risk mitigation in some detail.

Mitigating risks

5.1 Introduction

Mitigating risks, or lessening their adverse impacts, is at the heart of the effective management of risk. Beyond this, risk mitigation is an essential component of human behaviour because, in order to survive, human beings are, by and large, risk averse. Many normal day-to-day activities are affected by risk mitigation, e.g. the act of taking an umbrella when going out. Unfortunately in business activities risk mitigation is sometimes undertaken only at a rather superficial level. If more attention were paid to it, fewer business activities would end in disaster. It is not sufficient just to 'take a margin' for risk, since this results in little risk mitigation being done.

5.2 The risk mitigation strategy

If implemented correctly a successful risk mitigation strategy should reduce any adverse (or downside) variations in the financial returns from a project, which are usually measured by NPV or IRR. However, risk mitigation itself, because it involves direct costs like increased capital expenditure or the payment of insurance premiums, might reduce the average overall financial returns from a project; this is often a perfectly acceptable outcome, given the risk aversion of many investors and lenders. A risk mitigation strategy is the replacement of an uncertain and volatile future with one where there is less exposure to adverse risks and so less variability in the return, although the expected NPV or IRR may be reduced. However, increasing risk efficiency by simultaneously improving the expected NPV or IRR and reducing the adverse volatility is sometimes possible and should be sought. Risk mitigation should cover all phases of a project from inception to close-down.

5.3 Ways of mitigating risks

There are four main ways in which risks can be dealt with within the context of a risk management strategy. Risks can be

- reduced or eliminated
- transferred (e.g. to a contractor or an insurance company)
- avoided
- absorbed or pooled.

There is also the question of whether it is worth carrying out research to reduce uncertainty.

Each of these ways of managing risk will be considered in turn, and the approach will be illustrated initially by examples drawn largely from the construction or asset creation stage.

5.4 Reducing or eliminating risks

This is often the most fruitful area for exploration. For example, could the design of the assets be amended so as to reduce or eliminate either the probability of occurrence of a particular risk event or the adverse consequences if it occurs? Or could the risks be reduced or eliminated by retaining the same design but using different materials or a different method of assembly? For example, if there is a manufacturing process which uses a chemical that could injure human health, the risk could be eliminated by changing to a safe chemical instead. Other possible mitigation options in this area include: a better labour relations policy to minimise the risk of stoppages, training of staff to avoid hazards, better site security to avoid theft and vandalism, advance ordering of key components, noise abatement measures, good signposting, liaison with the local community, locating staff in more than one building, etc.

5.5 Transferring risks

A general principle of an effective risk management strategy is that commercial risks in projects and other business ventures should be borne wherever possible by the party which is best able to manage (and thus mitigate) them. Contracts and financial agreements are the principal way in which risks are transferred. The use of contracts in this way is discussed in Section 9.9. It may be worth considering the use of companies specialising in risk transfer. Another possible way to transfer risks is to pass them to an insurance company which, in return for a payment (premium) linked to the probability of occurrence and size of hazard associated with the risk, is obliged by contract to offer compensation to the party affected by the risk. Insurance cover can range from straight insurance for expensive risks with a low probability (e.g. fire), through performance bonds, which ensure that the project will be completed if the contractor defaults, to sophisticated financial derivatives like hedge contracts to avoid such risks as unanticipated losses in foreign exchange markets. Insurance is discussed in greater detail in Appendix 5.

To illustrate how insurance can help to improve a sponsor's risk profile, consider the following highly simplified example. Suppose that a project has a positive NPV of between £20 million and £60 million, depending on the outcome of various events. In addition, however, there is a 2% risk that a specific event will occur during construction which would cost £90 million. If this were to happen, the result would be a reduction in the NPV of the project to a figure between minus £70 million and minus £30 million; in other words,

there would be a substantial net loss on the project.

Now suppose that an insurance company offers to cover this risk for a single premium of £4 million. Most sponsors would probably consider this a worthwhile course of action because it would change the risk profile to one where there was no possibility of loss but an expected positive NPV of between £16 million and £56 million.

5.6 Avoiding risks

The most obvious way of avoiding a risk is to avoid undertaking the project in a way that involves that risk. For example, if the objective is to generate electricity but nuclear power stations, although cost-efficient, are considered to have a risk of producing catastrophic consequences that is thought too high, even after every precaution has been taken, the practical solution is to turn to other forms of fuel to avoid that risk. Another example would be the risk that a particularly small contractor would go bankrupt. The risk could be avoided by using a well-established contractor instead for that particular job.

5.7 Absorbing and pooling risks

Where risks cannot (or cannot economically) be eliminated, transferred or avoided, they must be absorbed if the project is to proceed. There normally needs to be sufficient margin in the project's finances to cover the risk event should it occur. However, it is not always essential for one party alone to bear all the absorbed risks. Risks can be reduced by pooling them, possibly through participation in a consortium of contractors, when two or more parties are able to exercise partial control over the incidence and impact of risk. Joint ventures and partnerships are other examples of organisational forms for pooling risks.

5.8 Reducing uncertainty

The above discussion of the mitigation options assumes that all the risks are known and can be quantified reasonably accurately. In practice, however, this is often far from being the case. Sometimes there will be a degree of uncertainty about which risks might occur that could significantly affect the project. Very often there will be uncertainty about the likelihood and impact of some of the major risk events which have been identified. One of the options in such circumstances may be to carry out research in order to reduce the extent of the uncertainty. Such research should be properly focused and costed: however, once it has taken place, it is a 'sunk cost' which should not figure in the capital cost of the project for purposes of analysis. A feasibility study is a classic example of such research.

Take as another example a proposal to erect a new building in London on the site of an existing one which is to be demolished. The new building will need much deeper foundations than the existing one. Preliminary calculations suggest that the financial viability of the project is likely to be critically dependent on the capital cost of the new building, which in turn will depend to a large extent on how easy it is to construct the foundations. An obvious option, in order to reduce uncertainty, is to arrange for the site to be investigated at the outset by studying maps of underground rivers, water mains, gas pipes, cables and railways, and perhaps by drilling below the floor of the existing basement to take soil samples. Such action will not reduce the true underlying risks associated with the foundations but it may well reduce uncertainty sufficiently to enable the project to proceed. Some other ways of dealing with uncertainty are discussed in Appendix 1.

5.9 Mitigation of non-construction risks

Construction is only one relatively short phase in the total life of a project, which extends from the first identification of the opportunity, through appraisal, planning and preparation to design, construction, operation and then close-down. Although the asset-creation stage is clearly important, risks exist in all of the other phases of the project and are often of greater significance. Many projects have been relatively robust with respect to construction risks but have been totally compromised by shortfalls in operating revenues. Some of the non-construction risks which could arise at the operating stage include

- inadequate forecasting of revenues
- fraud
- high operating costs due to high maintenance
- competition from other operators eroding market share and therefore revenues
- natural disaster (e.g. hurricane or earthquake)
- product obsolescence
- managerial incompetence
- reduction in use due to economic downturn.

There is no feasible all-inclusive list of risks available because new risks are arising all the time. Brainstorming sessions are essential to identify all risks which might arise as far as possible.

Mitigation measures which might be taken to tackle the various risks outlined above vary. For some risks an appropriate mitigation strategy is obvious. Natural disasters are best insured against. Fraud by employees is best prevented by having tight and effective financial control systems and can also be covered to some extent by insurance. The risk of high maintenance costs might be mitigated by changing the balance of capital to current costs in the specification of the construction of the project, thus 'over-engineering' the project. For some of these risks – product obsolescence or competitive pressure, for example – there may be no appropriate mitigation strategy: they are normal commercial risks and although they could in theory be insured against, the premium would be prohibitively expensive.

5.10 Use of financial structures to share risks

Various sources of funding are traditionally associated with different types of risk. Hence providers of each category of funding tend, through experience, to be comfortable with certain categories of risks. Conversely, when asked to price unfamiliar risks, funders are likely to adopt a very conservative view, often simply the worst case scenario. A bank, for example, is likely to take a very conservative view of the future sales of a product to be manufactured at a new factory which it is being asked to finance. The manufacturer, however, is relatively well versed in market risk for the product, and is in a much better position than the bank to understand the risk and will value it appropriately. Consequently, not only the ability of each party to manage and bear the cost of each risk should be considered, but also the value that each party attaches to carrying the risk should be borne in mind when allocating risks.

5.11 Developing a risk mitigation strategy

Each option for mitigation should be evaluated, assessing
- likely effect on risk, consequence and expected value
- feasibility and cost of implementing the option
- overall impact of each option on cash flows.

Often the cost of mitigation has to be incurred before – possibly long before – the benefits are felt. Indeed the benefits may never be certain, because it is often impossible to say whether the risk event would have occurred had the measure not been adopted. For example, installing a prominent burglar alarm might deter burglars but we will never be certain this has happened.

Sometimes risk mitigation actions generate secondary risks of their own, which need to be taken into account (and possibly mitigated). For example, the use of a safer chemical in a manufacturing process may carry the risk of supply problems if there is only one source.

The most effective option or options, including non-mitigation (i.e. absorption) where appropriate, should be chosen and recorded (with reasons) in the risk register. An action plan should be drawn up for each option.

The scope for dealing with some risks as a group should be explored. For example, a number of risks may be dealt with simultaneously by placing a financial agreement for funding, a construction contract or an operating franchise.

Those risks which warrant an in-depth study of possibilities for mitigation should be selected. Generally these will fall into two groups.
- Those risks where there are apparently worthwhile mitigation options but where confirmation is needed of their feasibility or cost (e.g. that external parties are prepared to enter into commitments on the terms assumed).
- The residual risks which are significant contributors to the downside volatility of NPV but for which no satisfactory mitigation measures have yet been identified.

The above should form the basis for a risk mitigation strategy, comprising all of the actions and the associated implementation plans, and include a statement showing the costs and benefits of each mitigation measure. The probability distribution of NPVs can then be recalculated and consideration given to whether a better result can be obtained by excluding those mitigation actions which have a high cost but limited beneficial effect on volatility. Some risks may need to be absorbed, unmitigated or only partially mitigated, because complete mitigation would be impracticable or too costly.

Thus risk mitigation is essentially a practical subject but a complex one, where there is a need for a methodical approach, clear thinking and imagination.

The principles of risk mitigation can be illustrated by considering one particular area. Many large scale computer projects have gone wrong in recent years (particularly in the public sector, where some high-profile schemes have been abandoned or delayed, with vast cost and reputational damage). Some suggestions for risk mitigation in future schemes of this nature are set out in Appendix 6.

5.12 Residual risks

Residual risks are those remaining after mitigation measures are taken. The RAMP team needs to assess the overall impact of residual risks by using the same techniques set out above. The results should be recorded in the risk register. Any new assumptions should be entered in the assumptions list. It is very important to ensure that the assumptions are comprehensively listed including any implied assumptions. Consideration needs to be given to the risk of assumptions proving false and this will necessitate further detailed analysis in the same way as for other risks.

The residual risks should be evaluated making allowance for the result of adopting the selected mitigation measures, and bearing in mind secondary risks and the cost of each measure. Their significance for each investment parameter can be determined by the use of judgement, or a technique like scenario analysis or Monte Carlo simulation which can be used to estimate a

probability distribution. The results of such research should be entered in the risk register, and are referred to as the residual risk analysis.

For each major activity in each stage of the investment life-cycle, an estimate should be compiled of the potential impact of unexpected risks, based on experience and the complexity and uncertainties associated with the activity. Unexpected risks include those foreseen risks which have not been measured or have been measured with a low degree of confidence. These should be consolidated into contingency allowances for unexpected risks.

Using the investment model, the overall impact of the residual risks on the investment (e.g. in terms of whole-life NPV) should be determined, with sensitivity analyses performed on the assumptions and estimates, and with account being taken of any contingency allowances.

With this data (expected value of the project's NPV, the estimated volatility, the reliability of its measurements, the results of the sensitivity testing and the potential consequences of the major risks), consideration must be given to whether the investment is still worthwhile or whether there is a version of the investment which would achieve (or nearly achieve) the same objectives with higher expected NPV and less downside volatility. The results of this work should be recorded in the risk mitigation strategy.

5.13 The investment submission and decision

The investment submission on which the decision to proceed or not will be based should bring together
- a description of the project and its baseline (see Section 3.2)
- a description of the most significant risks and how it is proposed to mitigate them (see Section 5.11)

- a description of the residual risks and the effect they will have on NPV (see Section 5.12)
- if there are significant alternative options, a recommendation on which should be chosen
- a recommendation on whether the project should proceed
- matters outside the scope of RAMP (e.g. how the project will be financed).

The final stage is to obtain formal approval from the client and any other key stakeholders (e.g. investors or lenders) for proceeding with the project. The decision-makers will take account of both the arithmetical results obtained and a range of intangible factors including

- the extent to which approximation and 'guesstimates' have had to be introduced into the arithmetical work, leading to possible unreliability of the numerical results obtained
- 'political' factors
- the feasibility of the project and risk mitigation actions
- any known biases on the part of those who have assigned numerical values to individual risks
- the results of discussion with those closely involved in analysis of the risks of the project
- additional knowledge (if any) which was unknown to the risk process manager
- 'hunch' and experience.

Planning for risk control

6.1 Risk response plan

Once the decision to continue with the project has been taken, a risk response plan is needed to minimise the probability of, and contain the impact of, all the remaining risks which cannot economically or practically be avoided, transferred or otherwise prevented. For each residual risk or area of risk, as set out in the residual risk analysis, overall responsibility for the risk should be assigned to an appropriate 'risk custodian', with other parties possibly delegated with responsibility for monitoring and controlling specific risks within the risk mitigation strategy. It should also be the responsibility of the risk process manager (or possibly one of the risk custodians) to monitor any changes which may be necessary in the key assumptions on which previous risk reviews have been based, as set out in the assumptions list.

In consultation with the risk custodians and other designated parties, the following should be devised

- containment plans to minimise the risks and their impacts.
- contingency plans to deal with specific residual risks should they occur and for each the 'trigger' events (or circumstances in which the contingency plans will be implemented) should be defined
- contingency budgets for the potential impact of the residual risks on each of the principal parameters of the investment.

It may be necessary to appoint the members of a 'crisis committee' to deal promptly with critical, potentially disastrous situations should they arise. Any restrictions on the committee members' level of authority should be carefully defined and reserve members should be appointed in case committee members turn out to be unavailable when a crisis arises.

The final step is to assemble containment plans, contingency plans and contingency budgets into a risk response plan and seek the approval of the client and other key stakeholders for this.

6.2 Risk review report

At the end of the risk review, the risk process manager will critically assess the effectiveness of the review and the manner in which it was conducted, drawing lessons from the problems experienced and suggesting improvements for future risk reviews. This will be achieved, partly by reviewing the risk diary and other documents produced, and partly by discussion with the client's representative and each of the other main participants. A formal risk review report should be compiled outlining the results of the review – including the main risks and their likely effects, the overall riskiness of the investment, and the main lessons which have been learned.

The risk review report should be considered in detail by client representatives responsible for the investment. In the light of the report, the client will need to decide when the next risk review will take place and how it should be conducted.

6.3 Communicate strategy and plans

Finally, the relevant parts of the residual risk analysis, risk mitigation strategy and risk response plan relating to risks assigned to each risk custodian and other parties involved in executing the

RISK ANALYSIS AND MANAGEMENT FOR PROJECTS

strategies and responses should be extracted. The risk custodians and other parties involved in executing strategies and responses should be supplied with the appropriate extracts. Verification must be obtained that these have been received and understood, and that those concerned are committed to undertaking the required action. All those involved should be encouraged to comment on or make suggestions about the residual risk analysis, risk mitigation strategy or risk response plan. If necessary, these documents should be revised to reflect the suggestions.

Managing risks

7.1 Implementing risk strategy and plans

A rigorous and comprehensive structure for implementing the risk strategy is essential if the strategy is to be carried out successfully. A lack of attention to this could result in the failure of the project.

The results of the risk review – notably, the residual risk analysis, risk mitigation strategy and risk response plans – are used to manage risks as part of the mainstream management of the investment. However, it is essential that the risk analysis, strategies and plans continue to be monitored and updated regularly as risk exposures change and risk events occur in between risk reviews. The organisation and processes for doing this must be embedded in the procedures for managing the investment as outlined below.

The risk mitigation strategy and the risk response plan must be fully integrated with the management systems and processes which determine the principal activities of the client (whether these are concerned with investment, project management or the operation of a finished facility). It is vital that there is full accountability with single responsibilities and accountabilities assigned to named individuals for each action. In particular, it is important to ensure that there is effective follow-up to verify that the various plans and actions previously determined are implemented in a timely and satisfactory manner – e.g. that contracts, financial agreements and insurance policies are concluded, 'trigger events' are observed, and payments made.

It is also important that, where special or exceptional actions are needed to deal with risks

which cannot effectively be integrated within the mainstream management processes, clear responsibilities and accountabilities should be assigned with reporting lines, or at least effective channels of communication, to the mainstream management. In addition, any exceptional actions, required to contain or respond to risks outside the scope of main management activities, must be co-ordinated with the main activities. Any significant changes or developments during the implementation of the risk mitigation strategy and the risk response plan should be reported promptly to the risk process manager.

7.2 Monitoring and controlling risks

The key task at this stage of RAMP is the monitoring of risks included in the residual risk analysis, risk mitigation strategy and the risk response plan. It must be verified that these are adequately resourced and effectively implemented. Other risks also need to be monitored regularly including those in the remaining stages of the investment life-cycle – not only the risks occurring in the present stage. Any significant changes in risk should be reported and assessed immediately. For example, the project may have to be abandoned half-way through construction if the risk that the facility may not be required increases sharply or if the risks in respect of operating revenue increase. Care must also be taken to ensure that there is a mechanism for identifying any new risks which may arise as a result of external developments.

Regular monitoring of risks can be undertaken by studying events, situations or changes (sometimes called 'trends') which could potentially affect risks during the normal management and progress of an investment. These trends can be exposed through

- site visits
- progress reviews
- design meetings
- correspondence
- negotiations with contractors
- ground surveys
- market research exercises
- tests
- reports on other similar investments.

These trends must be systematically identified, analysed and monitored on a regular basis by scrutinising reports, letters, and notes on visits, meetings and telephone conversations. The results are entered in trend schedules. Ideally, these should be considered at regular progress meetings (say weekly) involving key members of the management team. The trends can be usefully categorised as

- *Potential (category P):* to be assessed or observed more closely.
- *Expected (category E):* mitigation or response measures to be taken.
- *Committed (category C):* measures taken and then either treated as changes to the

investment baseline plans, after evaluating and allowing for their impact, or provided for in the risk mitigation strategy or risk response plan.

At each subsequent progress review meeting, the 'trends' will be considered and may be eliminated or moved into another category. Generally, newly identified 'trends' start in category P and then move first into category E and then into category C.

As progress is made through the investment life-cycle, it is necessary to revise the residual risk analysis, risk mitigation strategy and risk response plan, and to release contingency budgets, as some risks materialise and other risk exposures change or disappear. When problems or significant changes in scope occur it will be necessary to revise some parts of the residual risk analysis, risk mitigation strategy and/or risk response plan. Regular reports on progress, problems and changes should be submitted to the client's representative and other key stakeholders (notably the project manager and operations manager). The risk diary will be updated regularly by the risk process manager.

Finally, the fundamental merits of the investment – whether or not it is worthwhile – should be continually assessed and a risk review set in hand when events occur which appear to have significantly altered the risk profile of the project.

Closing-down phase

At the end of the investment life-cycle, or on prior termination of the project, a retrospective review will be made of the investment (in terms of its success and risk history) and of the contribution and effectiveness of the RAMP process itself as applied to the investment.

8.1 Assessing the performance of the investment

The risk process manager, in conjunction with the client's representative, will first evaluate the performance of the investment, comparing its results with the original objectives. Using risk review reports and the risk diary, an assessment will be made of the risks and impacts which occurred in comparison with those anticipated, highlighting risks which were not foreseen or grossly miscalculated.

8.2 Reviewing the RAMP process

The risk process manager will then critically assess the effectiveness of the process and the manner in which it was conducted for this investment,

drawing lessons from the problems experienced and suggesting improvements for future investments. This will be done, partly by reviewing the RAMP process plan, risk diary, risk review reports and other documents produced, and partly by discussion with the client and each of the other main participants.

The results of the review will be recorded in a RAMP close-down report, which can be easily referred to for future investments. Copies of the report should be circulated to all parties involved and then signed off by every party as an agreed record of events.

8.3 Prematurely terminated projects

Some projects will be terminated as soon as the initial risk review has been completed, because the risk–reward ratio is not deemed to be sufficiently attractive, and other projects will be terminated before the end of their planned life-cycle because of adverse developments. The production of a RAMP close-down report as a guide for other projects is likely to be particularly valuable in these circumstances because the most critical events in the history of the project will have occurred recently.

Applications and case studies

9.1 Introduction

This chapter discusses the application of RAMP in practice. It illustrates the uses to which RAMP can be put by reference to case studies. A summary of the key points which emerged from visits to practitioners in several large corporations follows and then a description is given of how RAMP can be applied to individual projects and to a series of projects. The importance of risk management and evaluation in the Private Finance Initiative is discussed. Next comes an indication of the scope for application of RAMP techniques in other circumstances, including concessions and franchise operations, and 'soft' projects not involving the construction of physical assets. Finally, there are a few thoughts on how the RAMP process should influence, and be influenced by, considerations relating to the contracts which will be entered into by the various parties concerned with the project.

9.2 Hypothetical case studies

Some hypothetical case studies have been prepared to illustrate how RAMP can be applied in practice. The examples are necessarily much simpler than real-life exercises, but they demonstrate the general approach recommended and highlight some important points. They also show how the RAMP methodology can be integrated with suitable investment models, in order to evaluate the risks financially and thereby enable rational decisions to be made about risk mitigation and whether the project should proceed.

The first case study concerns the introduction of a new computer scheme at a company. The project is relatively small and a simplified application of RAMP is appropriate, in conjunction with a NPV investment model. The process is shown in Appendix 7. The project has potential upsides and downsides, and these are evaluated by straightforward scenario analysis. An option for risk mitigation is explored and it is shown what the financial effect would be on the various outcomes if this option were adopted. Whether the risks should remain unmitigated or not would, in this example, depend upon the sponsor's attitude to risks of this size.

In the second example the case being examined is the building of a tolled road bridge across a river estuary which is at present served only by car ferries. Two large towns are separated by the river and the new bridge will substantially reduce the journey time between them. There are three alternative sites for the new bridge. Details of this case study are set out in Appendix 8, which also illustrates how to apply an investment model.

A preliminary appraisal of the project proceeds by making some simple calculations, using the present ferry tolls as the tolls for the bridge. These calculations suggest that the project may be marginally viable for two of the possible sites but not the third. However, a high-level risk assessment results in the rejection of one of the two more favourable sites.

The team then identifies and analyses the risks, and a mathematical model is constructed to simulate the traffic flow expected in various circumstances. A risk mitigation exercise leads to the conclusion that one of the principal options is to buy up the existing ferry company in order to prevent the bridge being undercut in price with a resulting loss of traffic. Buying up the ferry company has its own risks and these are evaluated and a mitigation plan developed for them.

This example highlights the following points.

- The need for high-level consideration of the project at an early stage, so as to reject unworkable options and save abortive work.
- The use of an iterative approach in the analysis, gradually getting into greater depth.
- The possibility that the earlier stages of risk analysis will lead to a change in the scope of the project in order to minimise risks.
- The fact that, although the calculations are an important input to the decision, a range of intangible factors must also be taken into account by the decision-makers
- The use of scenario analysis and the need for the scenarios with the more serious potential consequences (even if they are unlikely to occur) to be specially considered.
- The use of group brainstorming to generate 'key scenarios' and risk mitigation options.
- The need to analyse the 'secondary risks' which result from changes in the scope of the project or from the risk mitigation options selected.

A more elaborate case study, illustrating the use of RAMP methodology and the scenario method, was set out in an article by one of the authors of this handbook (*Private Finance Journal*, **1**(1), January 1996, pages 48–56, article by Chris Lewin). This related to a hospital project and showed how the public sector could evaluate the net benefits of the project on the alternative bases of carrying out the project itself, or accepting the provision of a service by a private bidder who would make the necessary investment.

9.3 Company visits

Several visits were made by the authors in 1998 to large companies in order to see how they assessed their projects; sincere appreciation is expressed to those companies who helped in this way. The

organisations visited included Railtrack, Shell UK, the Norfolk and Norwich NHS Trust, and the Highways Agency. They were not, of course, applying RAMP methodology itself, but they had somewhat similar processes in place and were able to give some useful hints which would be equally applicable to users of RAMP. These can be summarised as follows.

- It is essential to take proper account of the potential legal and business environments within which the project will exist.
- Worthwhile projects, for which workable solutions to problems exist, can be turned down because of poor methodologies which do not fully explore the needs, benefits and costs.
- Properly focused research, rather than simply extrapolating past data, can provide confidence for all parties when assessing the business case and specific proposals.
- The end users need to be committed to the project at an early stage, to prevent abortive work. All the decision-makers also need to be involved at an early stage.
- Using a well constructed risk methodology can help to overcome the fears and reconcile the requirements of all the interested parties, and bolster their confidence in the project.
- The methodologies already in use, even by large organisations, sometimes do not fully meet RAMP principles and could usefully be overhauled.
- There is a need to consider the human factor in risk analysis and management and to guard against excessively optimistic or pessimistic assumptions. In particular one should be sceptical of estimates put forward by those who have a vested interest in the project proceeding or not proceeding. Some estimates may be distorted for reasons associated with the interaction between the personalities of the people connected with the project.

- Never rely completely on checklists – always have a brainstorming session as well, and ensure that no possibilities are ruled out.
- Risk workshops should contain a variety of people from different backgrounds.

If this last point needs underlining, the authors of the PRAM report (see Section 1.10) point out that perceptions of a specific risk will differ from one person to another, with specialists in particular domains sometimes underestimating risks within their speciality and overestimating risks outside it. Moreover, individuals may be wary of giving an honest and objective view of the extent of a risk, because they may feel they will attract ridicule or hostility which may possibly impact on their careers. A group decision about risk may be insufficiently cautious, because it can less easily be held to be the responsibility of any individual and no individual within the group wishes to be seen by colleagues to be unduly negative. The formal process may need to be modified to remove such elements of possible bias as far as possible.

9.4 Individual projects

The main practical question which needs to be determined in applying the RAMP methodology to individual projects is the degree of depth to which the analysis should be taken. The version of RAMP presented here would normally be well worthwhile for a major project, say one involving a capital investment of £ 10 million or more, provided that preliminary investigations proved promising. There is no denying that carrying out the full version of RAMP could be expensive, but for a major project the cost pales into insignificance beside the likely benefits. For small or medium-sized projects a simpler version of RAMP can be used (an example of which is shown in Appendix 7).

The main benefits of applying RAMP (in either its simple or full form) to an individual project are likely to include

- identifying new risk areas not previously considered
- making sure that serious and catastrophic risks are not inadvertently overlooked in the final stages of the analysis
- opening up the possibility of additional risk mitigation measures
- focusing on the overall risk profile of the project and not just individual risks, leading to a better chance of reaching the right decision on whether to go ahead
- providing evidence about the residual risks, which will help to convince financiers to back the project
- giving better control of the risks once the project has been authorised.

9.5 A programme of projects

Sometimes a company will undertake a series of projects, each of which may be substantial in its own right but constitutes a relatively small part of the company's overall investment programme. The RAMP methodology is still applicable in such circumstances, although the company may be less averse to risk on any individual project, taking a 'swings and roundabouts' view. This may mean that the company would be less willing to consider risk mitigation measures which reduce the expected net present value of a project. It may also mean that some of the research work can be reduced, since the risks identified for one project may well be applicable to some of the other projects. In other ways, too, it may be possible to standardise the working methods with a resulting saving of expense.

Suppose, for example, that a rail company was undertaking a track renewal programme consisting of a series of similar projects at different locations.

Clearly the programme as a whole would be likely to benefit from RAMP analysis, to identify and mitigate the risks common to all the projects. Each individual project could then be the subject of a 'mini-RAMP' exercise, which would involve an examination of the risks specific to that particular project.

9.6 The Private Finance Initiative

Over the last few years in the UK, the government has sought to have much of the public sector's capital and infrastructure investment delivered through a developing form of procurement and contract known as the Private Finance Initiative. Under the PFI, public sector bodies, i.e. central government departments, local authorities and other public sector organisations, contract with private-sector bodies who will provide a long-term service which involves (among other things) the need for long-term investment at the expense of the private sector contractor.

Negotiating these contracts is an essential part of the process and has as an overriding objective the achievement of 'value for money' to the taxpayer and the transfer of 'substantial' risk to the private sector contractor. There are two important public sector policy goals, which in effect serve as parameters on risk transfer:

• Achieving value for money for the taxpayer usually means that a given risk should be borne by the party which can assume and manage that risk most efficiently and effectively.

• Enough risk should be transferred to the private sector contractor to ensure that the asset created is capitalised on the contractor's balance sheet and not on the public sector's.

The PFI has heightened awareness of project risks in ways that public procurement hitherto has not been able to do, so that the identification, allocation and management of risks has grown to become an essential part of the PFI process.

A PFI contract is an agreement for the provision of services. For example, the requirement for a new hospital is defined as a requirement for clinical support services and for a prison as correctional services. This leaves the private sector free to determine the best form of investment to provide the required services, which may be a far more efficient or innovative way than the public body is capable of providing. The private contractor determines the best form of investment, which it will design, build, finance and operate in order to provide the service required by the public body. PFI contracts are typically let for long periods, often in excess of 25 years, in order to give the contractor time to recoup capital and make a profit.

For example, in a roads contract the private contractor builds and finances the road. It provides all services associated with the road, including all aspects of operation and maintenance, to the Highways Agency, which pays the contractor in the form of 'shadow tolls'. Roadside services, in the fields of leisure, catering and retailing, can be provided direct to the public by the contractor.

Hospital projects are quite different. The contractor provides an NHS Trust with a range of non-clinical support services, to be delivered in a hospital building which the contractor designs, builds, finances and operates. Clinical services continue to be provided by the Trust and therefore the two parties must work together effectively after the hospital comes into operation.

PFI projects are usually complex, requiring the interaction and integration of a multiplicity of agents, functions and time horizons. For example, the private contractor might be a loose consortium of organisations, operating together to provide the range of services required by the public body. Each of these individual organisations, and the public body itself, will have different corporate objectives, management structures, time horizons and risk profiles. A vast array of technical, legal, financial and organisational functions will need to be integrated.

Risk analysis and management is crucial to the success of PFI projects and the RAMP process can readily be used for this purpose by either the public sector body or the private contractor (or both). In fact there may sometimes be a good case for both the public sector body and the private contractor to agree fairly near the start of their negotiations that it would be sensible to obtain an independent RAMP analysis of the project as a whole, as a preliminary to sharing the residual risks between them.

During the negotiations on risk sharing the public body must evaluate the PFI bid and determine whether it offers better value for the public sector or the community as a whole than does the alternative of carrying out the investment and providing the service itself. Some of the key questions guiding this assessment follow.

- What is the expected net present value of the project to the public sector under each alternative?
- To what extent is the possibility of downside outcomes for the public body reduced if some of the risks are transferred to the private contractor?
- What risks would be retained by the public body and could they be successfully managed?
- Will the contractor be able to manage effectively the risks transferred to it and have the financial ability to do so? Is there a risk that the private sector consortium might break up?
- How can the best deal for the public sector be negotiated?

The article in the *Private Finance Journal* quoted at the end of Section 9.2 sets out a possible way of doing the necessary calculations using RAMP methodology.

The private contractor will no doubt wish to do its own assessment, and apply RAMP methodology in the same way as any sponsor would do for its own projects. In the risk identification phase, however, the contractor will wish to consider whether there are any special risks involved in entering into a long-term contract with the government over a period of many years, during which its political complexion might change significantly, and whether there are any ways of mitigating such risks.

Even if it has not proved possible to get an independent RAMP report which is jointly sponsored by both the public body and the private contractor, it will be useful to maintain a 'risk matrix' for the project. This expression is used in an entirely different sense from its meaning in the identification phase of RAMP methodology, and means in PFI negotiations an important working document which provides both parties with information on all identified and significant risks in the project and the current allocation of these at any given point in the negotiations. Before the PFI contract is finally agreed, both the public body and the private contractor will wish to consider risk mitigation measures, and here again the RAMP methodology provides an appropriate way to proceed for each party.

Once a PFI contract has been agreed between the public body and its private contractor, each party will need to control implementation and its own risks, and this can best be done in the way which is recommended in the RAMP methodology. There is an additional dimension, however, in that there will need to be joint risk reviews regularly between the public body and the private contractor, to take account of emerging developments. It may be desirable to appoint an independent risk manager who will advise the project board on this.

9.7 Concessions and franchise operations

Granting concessions and franchises allows a business to have access to greater resources, a wider skills base and new capital, while retaining some element of control. Although some franchises may be purely operating concessions without a need for investment, others may require the concessionaire to invest in plant and machinery or even infrastructure. In the latter case the contract may be for 20 years or more, to enable the concessionaire to recoup the cost of investment and make a profit. RAMP methodology is entirely applicable in such situations, both for the company granting the concession and for the concessionaire. For the company granting the concession, the risks include the possibility that the actions of the concessionaire will taint the business overall or that the concessionaire will become insolvent while owing the company money (perhaps while any initial financial assistance given to the concessionaire is still outstanding). The company will normally wish to mitigate at least the first of these risks as far as possible.

For the concessionaire, the amounts of investment being made may not be sufficient to justify any more than a simplified RAMP analysis, but the need for that may be great, since the failure of the franchise operation will often have financial consequences which are very serious for the concessionaire who may be very averse to major risks and wish to mitigate them as far as possible. Even if the concessionaire is making no investment at all, a full risk analysis and cash flow model will be necessary to set pricing.

9.8 Soft projects

An example of the application of RAMP to a 'soft' project not involving the construction of physical assets is a risk management exercise conducted recently in the pensions management department at a major public company. The management team decided to assess the ongoing risks associated with the pension funds at home and overseas,

with a view to adopting further risk mitigation measures where these could be financially justified.

The first step was for the management team to identify a list of risks. These ranged from fraud and crime, right through to the possibility of the administrative work getting behind because of a sudden shortage of resources or a sudden peak of work. The risks were then analysed, with members of the management team contributing their views on the probability or frequency of occurrence and the likely consequences if the risk event occurred. It was found that in practice most of the risks could be expressed as being 'likely to occur once every x years'. The next step was to classify the risks according to a risk assessment table with a view to prioritising the risks with the highest scores. Particular attention was paid to those risks which would have very serious consequences, even if the frequency of occurrence was estimated to be low.

Brainstorming sessions were arranged to discuss some of the options for mitigating these priority risks. This was perhaps the most valuable part of the whole process, in that a number of entirely new options for mitigation emerged, which had to be evaluated, having regard to the costs which would be incurred if they were adopted.

There are many other soft projects where RAMP methodology could play a vitally important role, for example the launch of a new business or a new product, or the acquisition of another business.

Where companies make annual reports to shareholders about the main risks facing the business, RAMP methodology is ideally suited for this purpose, since it is possible to regard a company's business as an ongoing project or a series of ongoing projects, each of which is amenable to a RAMP analysis. An additional benefit is that the RAMP analysis could reveal some risk mitigation options not previously considered, even for an ongoing business. It could also highlight those ongoing projects where (perhaps because of a change in the risk profile since original authorisation) the probability distribution of the net present values of the stream of future cash flows shows too high an overall risk to justify continuation of the project.

So how should one apply RAMP to an existing ongoing activity? The answer is that it is exactly the same as applying RAMP at the later stages of a project which has been the subject of RAMP reviews from the outset, except that there will be no previous baseline to which to refer. The essential additional step, therefore, is to establish that baseline, just as one would at the start of a new project (see Chapter 3). Part of the process necessary to the establishment of the baseline will be the collection together of the various papers which have been put together in the past in relation to the activity in question, insofar as such papers are still relevant to the future of that activity. All the cash flows taken into account in the financial analysis should exclude cash paid or received in previous years: in particular, any capital which has been invested in the activity in the past is a 'sunk cost' which is irrelevant in assessing the NPV of future cash flows and the probability distribution of such NPVs.

In some cases, in relation to an ongoing activity, it may not be essential to carry out a detailed financial analysis and the aim will be to concentrate on risk and its management alone. If this is the case, it may nevertheless be necessary to carry out some approximate financial calculations when considering an optimum package of risk mitigation, to ensure that the costs involved are reasonable in relation to the benefits obtained.

9.9 Contractual arrangements

Once a project has been authorised, it is normal for the interests of the various parties to be defined by contractual arrangements. It is important to ensure that these arrangements take full account of the

residual risks remaining after the mitigation measures have been taken, and that responsibility for each of these risk events, should it occur, is clearly identified. This will necessitate the drawing up of quite detailed heads of agreement between the parties and close liaison with the lawyers involved.

There are, of course, many ways in which the contractual arrangements could be structured. One of the classic ways of ensuring that the project sponsor is relieved of risk is to enter into a fixed price contract, whereby the contractor undertakes to provide the sponsor with assets or a service at a fixed price (which may or may not be index-linked in future years). The reverse of this is a cost-plus contract, whereby the sponsor pays the contractor whatever the job turns out to cost, plus a fixed percentage for profit. It may be thought that the fixed price contract is necessarily preferable from the sponsor's viewpoint, but inevitably the contractor will build in a safety margin (except, for example, during an economic recession, when a contractor may take non-profit business to keep the workforce together) and the contract may therefore turn out to be more expensive than a properly supervised cost-plus contract would have been.

Moreover, even a fixed price contract may turn out to involve the sponsor in added cost. This is because such contracts usually include various clauses designed to cover exceptional circumstances, and in practice such clauses often result in negotiations towards the end of the construction period on whether an additional payment to the contractor is justified. Moreover, there is usually a *force majeure* clause, under which the contractor cannot be held responsible for extra costs or loss of receipts arising from delays due to strike action or other actions deemed to be outside its control. Such risks need to be taken into account in the sponsor's RAMP analysis.

Where there is a long-term contract for many years, as is often the case if a concessionaire has paid for infrastructure, it is quite likely that totally unforeseen adverse circumstances may arise at some point. It may or may not be clear from the contract which of the parties must bear the responsibility for remedying the problem. Even if it is clear that the responsibility should rest with the concessionaire, it may be impossible to meet the extra cost without becoming insolvent, in which case negotiations with the sponsor will be sought to achieve a sharing of the extra cost. Such negotiations are also inevitable if the contract is not clear about who should meet the extra cost. This means that a long-term contract is always to some extent a true risk-sharing partnership between the parties, however closely the contract appears to define each party's responsibilities.

Even if, as is highly desirable, clear instructions have been given at the outset to the lawyers about the differing responsibilities of the parties for a variety of risks, it is essential to check the final draft of the contracts carefully, to ensure that extra risks excluded in the RAMP process have not been shown as the sponsor's responsibility. If they have, it may be necessary to rework the RAMP process somewhat, in order to check that the project is still viable.

Where one party is obliged under the contract to provide a service or facility which could imperil the project or the interests of the other parties if it is not delivered to the specified standards, the risks for the other parties may be mitigated by the inclusion in the contract of penalty clauses for non-performance. However, while such clauses may act as a deterrent to non-performance, they are not always effective in extracting the prescribed penalties and some residual risks for the other parties will remain.

Future development

10.1 Continuing development

The publication of this handbook is a first step in the development of the RAMP process, which has the potential to become an industry standard in the field of project appraisal and risk management. However, to become even more useful, the RAMP system will need to be further developed and regularly updated. Above all, it will need to learn from and build upon experience gained by its users. It is only by continuing dialogue (involving feedback) between users and developers of RAMP over time that RAMP can become a benchmark in its field.

10.2 Getting feedback

If sufficient numbers of RAMP users indicate that they would find it helpful, a continuing forum will be established, within which RAMP briefings and process development can continue. It will also be desirable to supplement the RAMP handbook from time to time with updated material to enable the assimilation of new knowledge and understanding gained in application of the system. This will be done in the first instance through the RAMP website (www.RAMPrisk.com). The opportunity for dialogue with users could be reinforced with the establishment of a RAMP Help Line offering initial advice on a non-commercial basis to users of the RAMP system if there is sufficient demand for such a service. In the longer run it is possible to envisage RAMP becoming established as an example of 'best practice' for the appraisal of projects, with the development of a system of accreditation of practitioners which could provide assurance to would-be investors and other potential stakeholders. In the meantime the working party would very much welcome any feedback from users of this handbook. Details of how to contact the working party are given in Section 10.4.

10.3 Wider professional involvement

RAMP has been jointly initiated by the Institution of Civil Engineers and the Faculty and Institute of Actuaries. There are other professional disciplines involved in engineering, construction, business, property and finance with much to contribute on risk. Should it be decided to develop RAMP further, the founding bodies would see merit in involving other partners and professional groupings in the process. It can only benefit all, since if one thing is certain it is that risk management will grow to become one of the key management disciplines in the future.

10.4 Contacting the RAMP working party

The RAMP working party can be contacted through either of the following.

Institute of Actuaries
Staple Inn Hall, High Holborn
London WC1V 7QJ
Tel: 020 7632 2100
Fax: 020 7632 2111

Institution of Civil Engineers
1 Great George Street, London SW1P 3AA
Tel: 020 7222 7722
Fax: 020 7222 7500

Glossary

Assumptions list: this is a key part of the risk register which lists the assumptions, both explicit and implicit, on which the RAMP analysis is based. It is updated as and when previous assumptions need to be modified or new assumptions have to be made.

Baseline: the set of assumptions and methods which are used as the basis for the evaluation of risk in a project and its subsequent management. Risk analysis is impossible without a baseline which would, for example, include information on the objectives of the project, values of key financial parameters like discount rates, assumed levels of cash flows, financial model adopted, etc. (see Section 3.2).

Brainstorming session: an intense and focused scrutiny of an issue with the aim of covering it as comprehensively as possible and, in particular, identifying and discussing risks which might not otherwise be considered in the absence of such an intellectually charged and spontaneous environment. A brainstorming session should normally be led by a 'facilitator' whose task is to encourage suggestions, avoid criticism, and generally create an atmosphere in which participants are motivated to put forward as many relevant ideas as possible. A useful technique is to divide the session into two phases. The first phase consists of the generation of ideas where participants put forward ideas but no discussion is permitted (except for clarification) and the ideas are listed on a flip-chart by the facilitator. The second phase of the session consists of constructive discussion of the listed ideas to identify those that deserve to be explored further.

Client: the party (or parties) sponsoring the project.

Discount rate: the rate of interest which is used to discount cash flows arising in the future to their present-day value. It is necessary to do this because, with positive interest rates, a sum of money which is invested will increase in value over time. Hence, the present value of money is less than its value in the future. The size of the discount rate will affect the appraised viability of those projects to which it is applied: broadly, the higher the discount rate the lower will be the present value of earnings (or benefits) arising in the future and the greater the negative impacts on project feasibility. The discount rate is determined pragmatically by the sponsor. Ideally it should take account (among other things) of the sponsor's cost of capital, the rate of inflation, interest rates and rates of return on investments throughout the economy. There is a difference between 'real' discount rates and 'nominal' discount rates. Real discount rates are used in conjunction with cash flows which are expressed in terms of present-day money values, with no allowance for price inflation. (The cash flows should, however, allow for increments in future over and above price inflation, e.g. real wage increases.) Nominal discount rates, on the other hand, are higher than real discount rates and are applied to cash flows which make specific allowance for future price inflation at an estimated rate (see also Appendix 2). Some theoretical considerations regarding the choice of an appropriate discount rate are set out in *Principles of Corporate Finance* by Richard A. Brealey and Stewart C. Myers, Irwin McGraw-Hill, 6th ed, 2000. See also the section 'Choice of discount rate' on page 75 of this handbook.

Expected value: see Appendix 1.

Hurdle rate of return: the minimum internal rate of return acceptable to the sponsor of a particular project.

Impact: see Appendix 1.

Internal rate of return (IRR): the return which can be earned on the capital invested in the project, i.e. the discount rate which gives an NPV of zero. This is equivalent to the yield on the investment.

Investment: the creation of real or tangible capital, for example in the construction of a building or a piece of machinery, which will generate a flow of goods and services to be consumed in the future. We also use the word 'investment' to mean the assets and business activity resulting from a specific project which has been financed by capital sums.

Investment life-cycle: the lifetime of a project from inception to ultimate termination (see Section 2.4). Often there is uncertainty about the length of time over which a project will be operating and assumptions will have to be made.

Investment model: a framework for evaluating the likely profitability of the investment (see Appendices 2, 7 and 8).

Likelihood: see Appendix 1

Mitigation: action either to reduce the probability of an adverse event occurring or to reduce the adverse consequences if it does occur (see Chapter 5).

Monte Carlo simulation: a method for calculating the probabilities of outcomes by simulation, running a model many times, using a computer. Appendix 2 describes a stochastic approach of this kind.

Net present value (NPV): the difference between the present value of the cash flows generated by a

project and its capital cost. It is calculated as part of the process of assessing and appraising investments (see Appendix 2, and specimen calculations in Appendices 7 and 8).

Pay-back period: the period over which the total cash flow receipts from a project equal the original investment (without discounting).

Present value: the value now of a future payment, after discounting it by a suitable discount rate to recognise that it is worth less than a payment of the same amount made now (see Appendix 2).

Probability: the likelihood or degree of certainty of a particular occurrence taking place during a specified time period. Independent probabilities relate to events which do not depend on other events which have occurred previously. Dependent probabilities are the probabilities of occurrence once previous specified events have occurred (see Appendix 1).

Probability distribution: a distribution which relates a range of particular outcomes to their likelihood. The most common probability distribution is the *normal distribution* which is shaped like the cross-section of a bell (see Appendix 1).

Project: Any organised business activity where an investment is made. It most commonly refers to the work of creating and operating a physical asset, such as a bridge or a building. However, it need not involve the creation of a new physical asset at all, for example if a company launches a new product which has been manufactured by existing assets. The project extends over the whole investment life-cycle of activity, not just the initial phases while the investment is being made.

RAMP: Risk analysis and management for projects.

RAMP close-down report: a report prepared by the risk process manager after the project has terminated (see Chapter 8 and Appendix 11).

RAMP process plan: a plan prepared at the outset by the risk process manager, which establishes the risk strategy and baseline. The plan is updated as the work proceeds (see Chapter 3 and Appendix 11).

Residual risks: those risks which are not avoided, eliminated or transferred in the risk mitigation strategy (see Section 5.12).

Risk: see Appendix 1 and Section 2.3.

Risk analyst: an individual whose primary task is the identification and evaluation of risks during the risk review.

Risk assessment tables: tables that may be used to allocate 'scores' to risks, to help in prioritising them (see Appendix 4).

Risk custodian: an individual who has responsibility for monitoring, controlling and minimising the project's residual risks.

Risk diary: a logbook maintained by the risk process manager which should, *inter alia*, contain a record of key events in the planning and execution of the RAMP process, any problems encountered and unforeseen risks which arose, the results of the risk reviews and ways in which future risk reviews or the RAMP process itself could be improved (see Section 3.1 and Appendix 11).

Risk event: see Appendix 1 and Section 2.3.

Risk management: the process of managing risks identified in the risk review using the risk mitigation strategy and the risk response plan (see Chapter 7).

Risk matrix: the presentation of information about risks in a matrix format , enabling each risk to be presented as the cell of a matrix whose rows are usually the stages in the investment life-cycle and whose columns are different causes of risk . A risk matrix is useful as a checklist of different types of risk which might arise over the life of a project but it must *always* be supplemented by other ways of discovering risks (see Appendix 3 for a specimen risk matrix, and the checklists on pages 71 and 90).

Risk mitigation strategy: an overall plan for mitigating the risks in the investment activity (see Chapter 5 and Appendix 11).

Risk process manager: the manager who will plan, lead and co-ordinate the RAMP process (see Section 2.10).

Risk register: a list of risks identified in the risk review process, including full descriptive detail and cross-references (see Chapter 4 and Appendix 11).

Risk response plan: a plan (prepared towards the end of the risk review) for controlling the risks once implementation begins (see Chapter 6 and Appendix 11).

Risk review: an overall assessment of the risks involved in a project, their magnitude and their optimal management. Risk reviews can in principle be held at any stage in the life of a project with each review building on the results of previous ones. Each risk review should be preceded by a risk review plan. Risk reviews should generate information for inclusion in the risk register, risk mitigation strategy and risk response plan. The results of a risk review should be set out in a risk review report (see Chapters 4, 5 and 6 and Appendix 11).

Scenario: a hypothetical sequence of events in the future.

Secondary risks: risks which arise from actions taken to mitigate other risks or from extensions to the original scope of the project. Secondary risks can sometimes be important and always need to be analysed in their own right.

Sensitivity analysis: a technique used to discover how sensitive the results from economic and financial models are to changes in the input values of the variables used to calculate the results. A high degree of sensitivity is a warning to interpret the results of the model with care and circumspection, especially because many of the input variables will themselves have been estimated and therefore be subject to error. Use of econometric models must not obscure awareness of their limitations and possible pitfalls, especially when they are being used for forecasting.

Stakeholders: those parties whose interests are affected by decisions about the operation of an asset which they do not necessarily own or enjoy property rights in. Stakeholder interests in a local factory would include (as well as the owner) the local community, workers, investors, bank, consumers etc. all of whom are liable to be affected by decisions made concerning the operation of the factory.

Stochastic model: see Monte Carlo simulation.

Strategic risk: see Appendix 1.

Trend schedules: schedules which are used during the implementation of the project to record factors which could change the future risk profile of a project (see Section 7.2 and Appendix 11).

Uncertainty: a source of risk derived from a lack of sufficient knowledge about the underlying probabilities of adverse events and/or their consequences (see Appendix 1).

Yield: see Internal rate of return.

Select bibliography

Adams J. *Risk*. UCL Press, London, 1995.

Association of Corporate Treasurers. *Cost of Capital.* 1997, 2 volumes.

Berny J., Townsend P.R.F. Macro Simulation of Project Risks – a Practical Way Forward. *International Journal of Project Management*, 1994.

Blockley, D.I. and Godfrey, P.S. *Doing it Differently; Systems for Rethinking Construction*. Thomas Telford, London, 2000.

Boyce T. *Commercial Risk Management*. Thorogood, London, 1995.

Brealey, R.A. and Myers, S.C. *Principles of Corporate Finance*, Irwin McGraw-Hill, 6th ed., 2000.

Central Unit on Procurement. *No. 41: Managing Risk and Contingency for Works Projects.* HM Treasury,1993.

Central Unit on Procurement. *No. 43: Project Evaluation.* HM Treasury, 1993.

Chapman C.B., Ward S.C. *Project Risk Management: Process, Techniques and Insights.* J Wiley, Chichester, 1997.

Chapman C.B. and Ward S.C. *Managing Project Risk and Uncertainty: A Constructively Simple Approach to Decision Making.* John Wiley & Sons, Chichester, 2002.

Chicken J.C. *Managing Risks and Decisions in Major Projects.* Chapman and Hall, London, 1994.

Confederation of British Industry. *Realistic returns: how do manufacturers assess new investment?* CBI, 1994.

Corrie R K. *Project Evaluation.* Thomas Telford, London, 1992.

Edwards L. *Practical Risk Management in the Construction Industry.* Thomas Telford, London, 1995.

Engineering Council. *Guidelines on Risk Issues.* London, 1993.

Flanagan R. and Norman G. *Risk Management and Construction.* Blackwell Scientific, Oxford, 1993.

Godfrey, P.S. Benefiting from Risk. *Structural Engineer*, 16 April, 2002.

Godfrey P.S. *Control of Risk: A Guide to the Systematic Management of Risk from Construction.* CIRIA, London, 1995.

Grey S. *Practical Risk Assessment for Project Management.* J Wiley, Chichester, 1995.

Hillson, D.A. Toward a risk maturity model, *International Journal of Project and Business Risk Management* **1** (1), 35-45, 1997.

James M. (ed.). *Risk Management in Civil, Mechanical and Structural Engineering.* Conference Proceedings, Thomas Telford, London, 1995.

Kahkonen, K. and Artto, K.A. *Managing Risks in Projects.* E and F.N. Spon, London, 1997.

Lewin C.G. *et al.* Capital Projects. *British Actuarial Journal*, 1995.

Lewin C.G. A Case Study. *Private Finance Journal*, **1** (1), Jan. 1996, 48–56.

McGrath, R.G. Falling forward: real options reasoning and entrepreneurial failure, *Academy of Management Review*, **24** (1), 13-30, 1999.

Moder J.J. and Philips C.R. *Project Management with CPM and PERT.* Van Nostrand, New York, 1970.

Project Management Institute *A guide to the Project Management Body of Knowledge*, 2000 edition. Project Management Institute, Newtown Square PA, 2000.

Raferty J. *Risk Analysis in Project Management.* Spon, London, 1994.

Ren H. Risk Lifecycle and Risk Relationships on Construction Projects. *International Journal of Project Management*, 1994.

Royal Society. *Risk – Analysis, Perception and Management.* Report of a Royal Society Study Group, London, 1992.

Sadgrove K. *The Complete Guide to Business Risk Management.* Gower Publishing Limited, 1996.

Savvides S. Risk Analysis in Investment Appraisal. *Project Appraisal*, **9** (1) , 1994.

Simon P., Hillson D., Newland K. (eds). *Project Risk Analysis and Management Guide (PRAM).* Association for Project Management, 1997.

Songer A.D. *et al.* Risk Analysis for Revenue Dependent Infrastructure Projects. *Construction Management and Economics*, 1997

Stewart R.W., Fortune J. Application of Systems Thinking to the Identification, Avoidance and Prevention of Risk. *International Journal of Project Management*, 1995.

Thompson P.A., Perry J.G. (eds). *Engineering Construction Risks: A Guide to Project Risk Analysis and Assessment.* Thomas Telford, London, 1992.

Thompson P.A., Perry J.G. (eds). *Engineering and Construction Risk: a Guide to Project Risk Analysis and Management – Implications for Project Clients and Project Managers.* Thomas Telford, London, 1993.

Uff J., Odams A. M. *Risk, Management and Procurement in Construction.* Centre of Construction Law and Management, Kings College, London, 1995.

Vaughan E.J. *Risk Management.* Wiley, New York, 1997.

Walker C., Smith A.J. (eds). *Privatised Infrastructure: the BOT Approach.* Thomas Telford, London, 1995.

Wilkie A.D. A Stochastic Investment Model for Actuarial Use. *Transactions of the Faculty of Actuaries*, 1986.

Wilkie A.D. More on a Stochastic Investment Model for Actuarial Use. *British Actuarial Journal*, **1**, 1995.

Woodward D.G. Use of Sensitivity Analysis in Build-Own-Operate-Transfer Project Evaluation. *International Journal of Project Management*, 1995.

Appendix 1: The meaning of risk

In order to understand and apply the RAMP process, it is necessary to understand the basic concepts associated with risk and some of the techniques used in its analysis.

Simple example

Suppose we wish to construct a bird table for the garden in the hope that it will enable us to see many birds from our window.

Baseline plans

First we prepare an outline design, and compile a budget and plan for its construction and installation. Then we consider the risks which could affect the cost and timing of the project, or our enjoyment of the results when the bird table is in use. This will involve identifying and analysing the risks, and then minimising their adverse effects.

Identifying risks

Risks can have outcomes which are more or less favourable than expected (referred to as 'upside' and 'downside' risks respectively). In the case of the bird table, examples of downside risks include

- suitable timber difficult to obtain
- costs more than expected
- takes too long
- construction proves very difficult
- is struck by lightning after erection
- birds hate it!
- timber soon rots
- tool breaks
- concrete below soil prevents erection
- neighbours complain about the birds
- new legislation prohibits bird tables
- something else goes wrong.

There are also such upside risks as

- materials cost much less than expected
- takes less time than anticipated
- lasts far longer than thought likely
- attracts more bird varieties than expected
- a neighbour offers to build it
- we find one second hand.

The risks differ considerably in nature. They can arise before and during construction, or after the bird table comes into operation. Some are quite likely, others extremely unlikely. Some are uncertain, in that they are very difficult to assess. For example, the chance of new legislation might seem very unlikely at first sight but could become a real possibility in the event of disease being found to be spread by birds. Some risks are trivial in their effect, while others if they occurred would spell the end of the project. Some risks are independent, but many are dependent on others (e.g. the risk of it taking too long is dependent on, among others, the difficulty of finding suitable timber).

To analyse the risk of the project taking too long, we need to look at all underlying causes of possible delay and their chance of occurrence. Then we can decide what action we can take to minimise the risks and their effects if they arise. For example, we could reduce the chance of construction proving difficult by designing the bird table in accordance with plans in a do-it-yourself magazine. Also we could buy two types of nails in case the first type proves unsuitable for parts of the construction. This would increase the cost slightly, and we would have to consider whether it is worthwhile.

Evaluating risks

We have talked about the 'chance' or 'likelihood' of

various things happening. What do we mean by this? Consider the chance of the hammer breaking during construction of our bird table. One approach would be to estimate the proportion of occasions on which the hammer had broken on other jobs. We would not have exact records but might be able to say that, based on past experience, the chance is between one in a hundred and one in two hundred. Or, not having made a bird table before, we might perceive the chance to be somewhat increased, say, to one in fifty, because we shall be using longer nails than normal. But suppose the hammer was weakened on the last job without our knowing; then the shaft may break next time it is used, so that the real chance may be as high as, say, one in two.

Faced with the possibility of neighbours objecting, we might visit them to discuss our plans in advance, to ascertain their attitudes and discover how they are likely to react. This, and the previous example, illustrate that additional knowledge can dramatically alter our perception of the risks we are facing. The cost of investigating the true risks can often be worthwhile in terms of giving confidence that the project's objectives can be met.

If we were in the business of constructing and selling bird tables, then we could build up records of risks based on our experience over a large number of units. For example, if we had sold a million and one hundred had been struck by lightning over a five-year period, then we could calculate that the chance of this risk event is one in ten thousand. We could thus evaluate the likely cost of offering to replace them free of charge. However, if one is constructing only one bird table, does it really matter what the risk is of a lightning strike? It probably will not happen anyway. The answer depends on how seriously we view the loss of our bird table. If we regard this prospect as disastrous, it may be worth paying a small insurance premium to cover the potential loss. If the consequences of the loss are regarded as trivial, we would probably be content to bear the risk ourselves without insurance.

Many more risks will no doubt be considered in practice, even for this simple project, before the first steps are taken. For a major project, there would be many hundreds, or even thousands, of individual risks to be considered.

Unforeseen events

However much effort is put into risk analysis, there is sometimes a totally unexpected event which can scupper our well-laid plans. In our example we completed and installed the bird table successfully. The birds liked it and flocked to it. But after a week we noticed the birds being attacked by sparrow hawks as they fed and this continued. As a result the bird table brought us no pleasure so it has now been taken out of commission.

This illustrates that in practice it is often the unanticipated risks which can destroy even a major project or render it obsolete or unprofitable. Identification and study of the *strategic* risks can often be the most worthwhile aspect to concentrate on, especially near the beginning of the project appraisal process. By strategic risks, we mean those risk events which could have very serious or catastrophic consequences, even if the probability of occurrence is thought at first sight to be low. The iceberg risk for the *Titanic* is an obvious example.

RAMP is a process which helps to identify, analyse and minimise the risks and then bring them under proper control. It puts all these different considerations into a logical framework so that they can be treated methodically without so much likelihood of important aspects being missed.

The concepts and issues illustrated by the above example are explained more fully in the following sections.

Defining risk

The word 'risk' can have a number of different meanings. Consider for example, the following statements

- there is a risk of rain today

- there is an 80% risk of rain today

- there is a risk of getting wet if it rains today

- there is a real risk to motorists from the weather which is forecast for today.

Each of these statements is using 'risk' in a different sense. Risk is commonly used as a synonym for 'hazard', 'danger' or 'threat', i.e. an undesirable event. It can also refer to the likelihood of an event occurring. A third meaning is the loss, injury or other outcome resulting from an event. Yet another usage is to describe the generality of volatility and uncertainty – the combined effect of all the individual risks in an investment or situation (i.e. the overall 'riskiness').

The 'R' in RAMP stands for the word 'risk' in the latter sense, meaning the potential impact of all the threats (and opportunities) which can affect the achievement of the objectives for an investment. RAMP analyses and responds to the uncertainty relating to the objectives – for both favourable and unfavourable effects. Thus, unlike the usual dictionary definition of 'risk' (which refers only to undesirable events), the RAMP interpretation of risk includes both downside and upside variations in the values involved (e.g. capital costs, revenue, net present values, etc.).

In analysing risks we are contemplating future events, the outcomes of which are therefore uncertain. We cannot generally predict with absolute confidence a particular outcome. Nevertheless, using relevant experience and judgement, we can usually define the range of possible outcomes, and then derive estimates of the likelihood and consequences of each, with a reasonable degree of confidence. This is the basis of risk analysis.

In their 1992 study the Royal Society used the word 'hazard' to mean a situation having the potential for human injury, damage to property, damage to the environment, or economic loss. They reserved the word 'risk' to mean a combination of the probability, or frequency, of occurrence of a defined hazard and the magnitude of the consequences of the occurrence. However, we have found it necessary to use the word 'risk' in the wider senses referred to above, in line with common parlance.

Key elements

There are four main concepts associated with evaluating risk.

- *Risk event:* a possible occurrence which could affect (positively or negatively) the achievement of the objectives for the investment

- *Likelihood:* the chance (or probability) of the risk event occurring within a defined time period

- *Impact:* the financial value of the effect of the risk event on one or more objectives if it occurs

- *Expected value:* the average impact of the risk event over a large number of similar projects (generally calculated as: likelihood x impact).

We shall explain each of these in turn, in the context of their use in RAMP.

Risk event

Risk events are the specific happenings that can influence the success of the investment, which therefore need to be identified, evaluated and mitigated as part of the risk analysis and management process. Examples are

- delay in tunnelling for a new underground railway due to unforeseen ground conditions

- overspend caused by increased cost of land acquisition

- intervention by regulator to limit price increases

- introduction of new statutory maximum noise levels

Each risk event can be triggered by one or more causes and can result in one or several outcomes. For the first three of the above examples, these could be as shown in Table 3.

As illustrated in Fig.6, there is a likelihood that each cause will lead to the event, and a further likelihood that if the event does occur it will result in each of the outcomes. Of course, several causes can arise together, increasing the chance of the event, and several outcomes can result from the event (e.g. a delay is usually associated with an extra cost).

Likelihood

Likelihood (or probability) is the degree of certainty that a risk event will occur during a specified time period. Typically it is measured on a scale of 0 to 100% (as in "there is an 80% chance of rain today") or, more usually, as a probability on a scale of 0 to 1, in which 0 represents an impossible event, 1 a certainty, and 0.5 an evens chance of occurring.

The theory of probability was originally developed for games of chance, such as tossing coins, drawing cards and spinning roulette wheels. For such cases, probabilities can be calculated easily by analysis. For example, when an unbiased coin is spun there are only two possible occurrences (ignoring the unlikely event of the coin landing on its edge) – a head or a tail. There is thus an evens chance that a toss will result in a head – i.e. the probability is 1/2. Likewise, the probability of getting a black King or Queen when a card is drawn at random from a pack of 52 is 4/52 or 1/13. In each case, the probability of a

Causes	Risk events	Possible outcomes
Unforeseen geological conditions Man-made obstructions Site flooding	Delay in tunnelling	Late completion Less time for installation of track and equipment Increased capital cost
Higher property prices More land required Unexpected need for decontamination	Increased cost of land	Overspend on capital budget Need to reduce scope
Reduced total investment Recent price rises Appeals from customers	Regulator limits prices	More customers Lower or higher revenue

Table 3. Risk events and possible outcomes

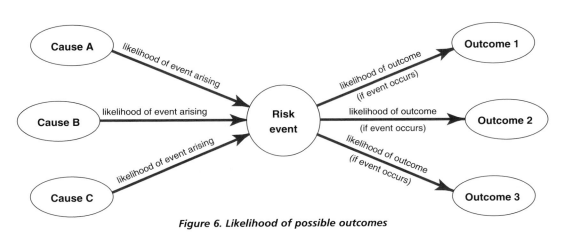

Figure 6. Likelihood of possible outcomes

particular outcome is calculated as

Number of occurrences which give rise to that outcome
_____
Exposure (i.e. number of possible occurrences)

This applies provided all occurrences are equally likely and mutually exclusive (i.e. no two occurrences can happen simultaneously). Such calculations can be confirmed by experience. For example, if a coin is tossed a large number of times, say 500, the proportion of *heads* is likely to be approximately 50% of the total, i.e. about 250. Of course, for real life events the estimation of probabilities is less clear cut, but similar principles can be applied. Generally, the best approach is to use observed frequencies, from experience of similar events, assuming that appropriate information can be obtained.

As an example, suppose we wish to estimate the probability that a new toll bridge spanning a river estuary will have to be closed due to high winds (in excess of 60 mph) on the day of the Royal Opening scheduled for 1 November. By consulting meteorological records kept at a weather station near the site of the bridge, we see that during the 20-day period around that date (i.e. from 10 days before to 10 days after mid-day on 1 November), over the last 10 years that records have been kept, there have been 17 days when winds have been stronger than 60 mph. Hence the probability of the bridge being closed because of winds is 17/(10 x 20)

or 17/200, i.e. about a 1 in 12 chance.

A crucial factor in deriving measures of probability is the validity of the assumptions which need to be made. So these must be carefully checked for realism, noted and monitored. If they change, the probabilities will need to be revised. An illustration of the probabilities and underlying assumptions for the above risk events is set out in Table 4.

Impact
As defined above, the impact of an event is the value of the effect of the risk event, if it occurs, on one or more of the financial parameters of the investment, e.g. on capital cost, revenue or operating cost. Thus impacts are derived by assessing the consequences of the outcomes of an event in terms of their financial consequences for the objectives. The impact can often be expressed as the NPV of the cash flows resulting from the outcomes. Table 5 gives an example.

Expected value
Any potential risk may or may not occur in a particular investment. In order to get a good idea of what we might reasonably expect to be the overall impact of any category of risks for an investment, we need some simple measure. That is given by the 'expected value', which is calculated by multiplying impacts by the associated probabilities of events. It is equivalent to the average impact of the risk event

Risk event	Probability	Assumptions
Head on toss of coin	1/2	Unbiased coin Properly tossed Does not end on edge
Black King or Queen on draw of card	1/13	Selected at random Normal pack of 52 cards
Toll bridge being closed at Royal Opening (in above example)	17/200 = 0.085	Closure enforced if 60 mph winds at any time in day Wind limit does not change Weather system unchanged over last 10 years

Table 4. Probabilities and assumptions for specific risk events

Risk events	Outcomes	Impact (NPV): £ million
Ground subsidence due to tunnelling for underpass	Damage to 6 buildings	Cost of compensation 2.0
New competitor enters market for bus service	Loss of passengers	Reduced revenue 3.7
Major contractor is bankrupt	Extra cost and delay for re-tendering	Increased capital cost 1.0 Loss of early revenue 1.5

Table 5. Impact of risk events expressed as the NPV of cash flows

Scenario	Probability	Impact	Expected value
Game cancelled	10%	−£2 000 000	−£200 000
Only one-third of seats occupied	30%	−£1 000 000	−£300 000
Seats fully occupied	20%	+£1 000 000	+£200 000
	60%		−£300 000

Table 6. Example of the calculation of expected value

Scenario	Net revenue	Probability
Game cancelled	−£400 000	10%
Only one-third of seats occupied	+£600 000	30%
Base case (two-thirds occupied)	+£1 600 000	40%
Seats fully occupied	+£2 600 000	20%
		100%

Table 7. Probability distribution of net revenue

which would result if we were to carry out a large number of identical projects.

Thus, for example, if the chance that a cricket ground will be unsuitable for a test match is 0.1 and the impact on revenue if the game is cancelled is estimated as £2 million, then the expected value of cancellation is £(0.1 x 2) million, that is £200 000.

More generally, where there are several alternative possible outcomes, the overall expected value is the sum of the expected values of each outcome. Let us illustrate this by returning to our test match. If the match takes place and all available seats are occupied, the gross revenues will be £3 000 000. There will be fixed expenses of £400 000 irrespective of seat occupancy or whether the match takes place. The base case, or most likely outcome (with a 40% probability), is that the match takes place with two-thirds of the available seats

occupied. The forecast net revenue is thus 2/3 x £3 000 000 less £400 000, i.e. £1 600 000.

There are three alternative scenarios being considered, namely that the match is cancelled, or that only one-third of the seats are occupied, or that all the seats are occupied. We can calculate the expected value of each scenario as illustrated in Table 6.

Thus the overall expected value of the risk scenarios is minus £300 000. To obtain the expected value of the net revenue from the match, we must deduct £300 000 from the base case forecast of £1 600 000, to leave £1 300 000.

Probability distributions

The expected value of £1 300 000 can be regarded as the average net revenue which would be obtained from each test match if a large number of matches were to be played. If only one match was due to be played, however, it would in addition be useful to look at the probabilities of occurrence of each of the possible outcomes, as in Table 7: this shows the probability distribution of the net revenue. It demonstrates that there is a 10% risk of losing £400 000 and this possible outcome needs to be taken into account by the sponsor before deciding whether to proceed or not. Also, the sponsor will want to take account of the 20% chance of gaining as much as £2 600 000.

Let us take as another example a specialist developer of high-quality houses. He has found from experience that, at current prices, he can sell the following proportions of his standard 'classic' houses at each price (to the nearest £100 000)

- 0.3 at £600 000
- 0.5 at £700 000
- 0.2 at £800 000.

This can be plotted as a probability distribution and as a cumulative probability distribution, as shown in Figs 7 and 8. The cumulative probability distribution shows the probability of selling at a particular price or less. Hence the chance of being able to sell at up to £750 000 is 0.3 + 0.5 = 0.8.

Thus, from the cumulative probability distribution, we can estimate that there is approximately a 50% chance that the selling price of a house will reach £690 000. In this example, this is the same as the expected value which is given by: £[(6 x 0.3) + (7 x 0.5) + (8 x 0.2)] x 100 000, i.e. £690 000.

Wherever practicable, recorded data is used to derive probability distributions, with adjustments if necessary to allow for future trends. However there are many cases where this is not feasible. In such cases, if the risks involved are such as to justify quantifying, then it is necessary to estimate the probability using judgement – ideally exercised by someone with expertise in the particular area concerned.

For example, we may wish to elicit from an art expert the probability distribution for the price likely to be realised at auction for a masterpiece owned by a charity of which we are patrons. Based on the method outlined by Chapman (1997), we may ask the expert to proceed as follows (for simplicity,

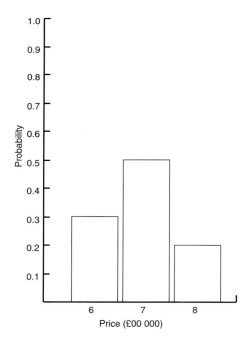

Figure 7. Probability distribution

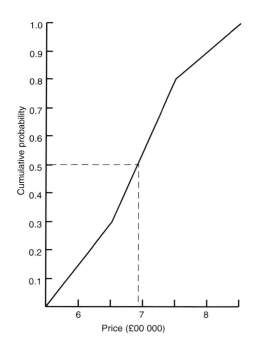

Figure 8. Cumulative probability distribution

ignoring here the possibility that the painting may remain unsold).

- Estimate the high-impact scenario (H) which has, say, a likelihood of 10% of being reached. For the painting assume this is £400 000.

- Next determine the low-impact scenario (L) for which there is only a 10% chance (say) of it not being exceeded. Let us presume this is set at £200 000 in our example.

- Then choose either one or two intermediate points – either one-half or one-third of the distance between L and H. We assume here one at £300 000.

- Decide on a class interval – usually this can be conveniently set equal to $(H - L)/2$ or $(H - L)/3$ depending on whether there are one or two intermediate points between L and H. For the picture, the class interval will be £100 000.

- Then (using expert judgement) assign estimated probabilities (ideally rounded to one significant figure) to each class in the range. These give for the masterpiece the following distribution (to the nearest £100 000).
  - 0.3 at £200 000
  - 0.5 at £300 000
  - 0.2 at £400 000.

The above discussion may seem to imply that any risk event has a single clearly defined impact if it occurs. However, in practice there is often a range of possible outcomes for an individual risk event, each of which has a different probability (i.e. there is a probability distribution for the risk). Furthermore, for each outcome of the risk event, there can be a range of impact values, each with its own likelihood of occurrence.

Combining risks

A primary aim of RAMP is to evaluate and manage risks affecting the overall investment. It is therefore essential to be able to aggregate a number of risks which could potentially affect each of the investment objectives. In order to do this, we need to quantify at least the most significant risks, understand the nature of their relationships if any, and then combine the probabilities so as to determine their collective effect.

There are two main rules for combining individual risks – probability 'addition' and 'multiplication'. These will be explained by assuming there are two events, A and B respectively, for which the probabilities of their occurring can be denoted as Prob(A) and Prob(B).

The 'addition' rule states

Prob(A or B or both) =
Prob(A) + Prob(B) – Prob(A and B).

The reason for subtracting Prob(A and B) is that Prob(A) includes the possibility that A and B occur together and so does Prob(B), so one Prob(A and B) is subtracted from the sum to eliminate double counting.

If events A and B are mutually exclusive, i.e. cannot occur together, then Prob(A and B) = 0, so Prob(A or B or both) becomes Prob(A) + Prob(B).

The 'multiplication' rule states

Prob(A and B) =
Prob(A) x Prob(B), provided A and B are independent.

By 'independent' we mean that the occurrence of one event does not influence the likelihood of the other. If, as often is the case, the events are not independent, then the multiplication rule becomes

- If B is dependent on A – i.e. the fact that A has occurred could affect the likelihood of B's occurrence, then

  Prob(A and B) =
  Prob(A) x Prob(B, given that A has occurred).

- If A is dependent on B – i.e. the fact that B has

| Scenario | Selling price of | | Probability | Total revenues: *£00 000 |
	1st home: £00 000	2nd home: £00 000		
A	6	6	0.3 x 0.3 = 0.09	12
B	6	7	0.3 x 0.5 = 0.15	13
C	6	8	0.3 x 0.2 = 0.06	14
D	7	6	0.5 x 0.3 = 0.15	13
E	7	7	0.5 x 0.5 = 0.25	14
F	7	8	0.5 x 0.2 = 0.10	15
G	8	6	0.2 x 0.3 = 0.06	14
H	8	7	0.2 x 0.5 = 0.10	15
I	8	8	0.2 x 0.2 = 0.04	16
			1.00	* + or − £100 000

Table 8. First estimate of probability distribution (assuming independence)

occurred could affect the likelihood of A's occurrence, then

Prob(A and B) =
Prob(B) x Prob(A, given that B has occurred).

Prob(B, given that A has occurred) and Prob(A, given that B has occurred) are called 'conditional probabilities' and will not generally be the same as the unconditional probabilities, Prob(B) and Prob(A).

As a simple example of using the above rules, we can calculate the probability of getting an odd number or a number less than three, or both, when we throw a six-sided die as follows.

Prob('odd' or 'less than 3' or both)

= Prob('odd') + Prob('less than 3') − Prob(both)

= 3/6 + 2/6 − 3/6 x 2/6

= 4/6 = 2/3.

In this case, Prob('odd') and Prob('less than 3') are treated as being independent. The above rules can be extended to cover the combination of any number of individual risks. However, combining risks which have probability distributions for a range of values gets more complicated. To demonstrate how this can be done, let us go back to the example of the house developer above. Suppose he plans to sell two houses over the next two months and wishes to estimate the probability distribution

Total revenue *£00 000	Scenarios	Combined probability
12	A	0.09
13	B, D	0.30
14	C, E, G	0.37
15	F, H	0.20
16	I	0.04
* + or − £100 000		1.00

Table 9. Result of first estimate of probability distribution (assuming independence)

for the total resulting selling price, assuming the two sales are independent. This can be done as shown in Table 8.

We now gather together the scenarios giving the same total revenues and hence arrive at the probability distribution shown in Table 9 for the total revenue.

As stated above, this assumes that the price of the second house is independent of that for the first. In practice, risks are rarely perfectly independent.

Two kinds of dependence can be distinguished, representing positive and negative correlation between the risks. Positively correlated risks tend to increase together, whereas negatively correlated risks move in opposite directions.

Let us now suppose the price of the second house has a 60% chance of falling within the same

| Scenario | Selling price of | | Probability | Total revenues: *£00 000 |
	1st home: £00 000	2nd home: £00 000		
A	6	6	0.30 (0.60 + 0.40 x 0.3) = 0.216	12
B	6	7	0.30 (0.40 x 0.5) = 0.060	13
C	6	8	0.30 (0.40 x 0.2) = 0.024	14
D	7	6	0.50 (0.40 x 0.3) = 0.060	13
E	7	7	0.50 (0.60+0.40 x 0.5) = 0.400	14
F	7	8	0.50 (0.40 x 0.2) = 0.040	15
G	8	6	0.20 (0.40 x 0.3) = 0.024	14
H	8	7	0.20 (0.40 x 0.5) = 0.040	15
I	8	8	0.20 (0.60 + 0.40 x 0.2) = 0.136	16
			1.000	*+ or – £100 000

Table 10. Second estimate of probability distribution (assuming dependence)

Total revenue: *£00 000	Scenarios	Combined probability
12	A	0.216
13	B, D	0.120
14	C, E, G	0.448
15	F, H	0.080
16	I	0.136
* + or – £100 000		1.000

Table 11. Result of second estimate of probability distribution (assuming dependence)

price bracket as the first house (due to word getting out) and only a 40% chance of being sold entirely independently. We would then have the situation

shown in Table 10 and the resulting probability distribution as is presented in Table 11.

This is *very* different from the preceding result based on an assumption of independence, as can be seen in Figs 9 and 10.

Many users of risk analysis tend to use techniques for aggregating risks which implicitly treat the risks as if they are completely independent. This can give seriously misleading results. Chapman (1997) points out that a high degree of dependence is typically encountered – up to 80% for costs and typically 50% for time related risks. Chapman proposes calculating the cumulative probability distributions for each of the

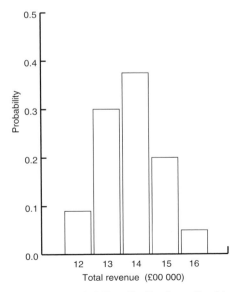

Figure 9. First probability distribution: all sold independently

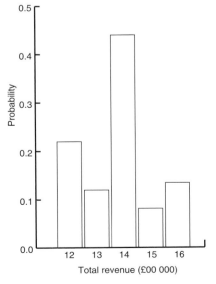

Figure 10. Second probability distribution: only 40% sold independently

Perceived risk distribution		Real risk distribution	
Value of outcome	Probability	Value of outcome	Probability
6	0.2	7	0.1
7	0.4	8	0.2
8	0.3	9	0.4
9	0.1	10	0.2
		11	0.1

Table 12. Perceived and real risk distributions

risks being combined and then deriving a weighted average cumulative distribution to represent the combination of the risks, using as weights, r and $r - 1$ to multiply the dependent and independent distributions, where r is the correlation coefficient. The coefficient can be based on calculation or judgement.

Real and perceived risks

Perhaps the most tantalising thing about risk analysis is that, in most situations, we do not, and cannot, know the real risks that we face. Even after exposure to the risk has taken place (whether the risk event occurred or not), we still do not know what the true risks really were. Specifically, we do not know what the real risk distribution is and what will be the specific outcome for a particular risk event if it occurs. Clearly, there is a difference between perceived risk and real risk. The former is what we estimate, the latter is the true risk which currently exists. See Table 12 for an example of possible differences between a perceived and a real risk distribution.

The average values of these risk distributions are 7.3 and 9 respectively, and let us assume that the actual outcome is a value of 7. The risk distribution histograms and the actual outcome, on common axes, are shown in Fig. 11.

When and if the risk occurs we know, of course, that it lies within the real risk distribution, but not where nor what the shape of the real distribution is. In this example, the perceived risk distribution is significantly different from the real one. Yet, when the actual result turns out to be 7 – approximately

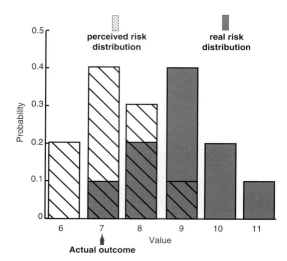

Figure 11. The outcome of the risk distributions shown in Table 12

equal to the estimated average value – it may be presumed, quite wrongly, that the perceived distribution was close to the truth.

Even if we had correctly estimated the risk distribution initially, it is distinctly possible that the distribution may have changed significantly before the risk exposure ends. That is why we need to be diligent in recording and monitoring the assumptions which underlie our estimates of risks, and why we need to reassess risks at regular intervals during the life of an investment.

The degree of difference between perceived and real risks depends on our level of knowledge about the risks and the situation in which they exist. We can sometimes improve our knowledge of the risks by carrying out further research in an endeavour to make our perception of the risks more closely match reality. Our success in estimating risks will depend on

- availability of valid data from experience
- our level of expertise in the area of risk
- our insight into the underlying causes and factors influencing the outcomes
- the extent to which the risks are stable or subject to change
- reliability of assumptions.

In view of such difficulties, it may be asked "Why bother?" The answer is that the risks are real and will not disappear, and so they cannot be ignored. Even if our attempts to measure risk are not entirely successful (and it is extremely difficult to measure our degree of precision), there is clearly enormous potential benefit in analysing and managing risk to the extent that is practicable. The precise probability of occurrence and the precise outcomes may be unimportant when it comes to mitigation, for example. Despite the difficulties of measurement, experience suggests that, properly executed, risk analysis and management is the crucial factor in successfully carrying through any investment.

Unforeseen and unknown risks

One thing is certain: for any major investment, it is unlikely to be possible to identify all of the risks which could arise. In virtually every project, problems occur which were not anticipated. Sometimes these can have a substantial impact on an investment, e.g. the tunnel collapse in constructing the Heathrow Express, which led to doubts about the NATM method of tunnelling and caused a substantial delay to the

Jubilee Line Project. Clearly it is important to attempt to identify as many risks as possible in advance, to be ever vigilant to spot new risks as they emerge, and to have quick and effective responses for dealing with risk events which do arise. Unexpected risks typically arise due to causes in the following categories, which therefore provide a valuable checklist to help prompt our attempts to identify such risks

- new laws, regulations or court judgments
- reactions of hostile interests
- freaks of nature
- physical environment proving unexpectedly harsh
- unforeseen man-made hazards
- new technologies
- malignant action by third parties
- project rejected for environmental or historical reasons
- unexpected financial, economic or political circumstances
- unexpected problems arising from design of physical assets
- unlikely accidents
- risks which could have been foreseen but were not
- breach of contract by investors, contractors, etc.
- fraud and crime
- inadequate organisation.

There is also the point that the risk event itself may have been foreseen, but the impact may prove unexpectedly disastrous.

Recognising that, at any time, we can be only partially aware of the totality of risks to which an investment is exposed, it can be useful to have the

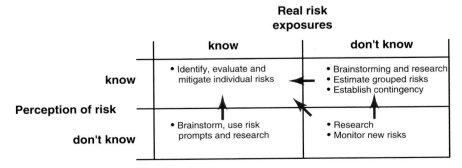

Figure 12. Degree of awareness regarding risk exposure

following model of our degree of awareness regarding real risk exposures.

As Fig. 12 indicates, there are four categories of risks, namely risks which we

- know we know (i.e. K/K risks)
- know we don't know (i.e. K/DK risks)
- don't know we know (i.e. DK/K risks)
- don't know we don't know (i.e. DK/DK risks).

Commenting on each of these categories in turn

- *K/K risks:* identify, evaluate and mitigate these risks using the RAMP process
- *DK/K risks:* conduct brainstorming sessions, use risk prompts (e.g. risk map, risk matrix, check lists and case studies), and undertake research to suggest possible risks which then are in K/K category
- *K/DK risks:* if not possible or practicable to identify and evaluate individual risks, then *either* estimate grouped risks (e.g. may make overall allowance for unspecified 'design' risks or 'commercial' risks) *or* allow for risks in a general contingency budget
- *DK/DK risks:* undertake research to identify risks and monitor emerging risks – which then are in category K/K, if they can be evaluated individually, or category K/DK, if they are better treated as part of a risk group or a general contingency allowance.

Mitigation of unquantified risks

How can one decide how much expense it is worth incurring on a particular risk management action, if one does not know the probability of occurrence of the event one is protecting oneself against? For example, is it worth designing a bridge to be slightly wider than is necessary at present, at significant extra cost, in order to have a better chance of coping with the risk of wider vehicles or a statutory requirement for wider traffic lanes?

Such questions are perhaps best approached by looking first of all at the financial impact if the risk

event were to recur, in this case probably little short of catastrophic, particularly if it happens near the start of the period of operation. Giving due weight to the consequences if the event were to happen at different points of time, let us take the average impact as £A. Suppose that the capital cost of the extra work is £B, where B is much less than A. Then, from a strictly mathematical viewpoint, if the chance of the risk event occurring during the project's life is greater than B/A, the extra work is worth doing. Thus we do not need to know exactly what the probability is, only that it is greater than B/A. It then becomes a question of judgement as to whether the probability is within this range or not.

However, this method of calculation would only be appropriate for a sponsor to whom a chance of B/A of losing £A is equal in value to the certainty of incurring a cost of £B. For some sponsors, particularly if the finances of the project are large in relation to the sponsor's own finances, the amount it may be worth spending to avoid a catastrophic loss would be increased.

One particular kind of uncertainty is the extent to which the project may be delayed (or even aborted or cancelled) because of the influence of other interested parties who may be hostile to the project or to certain aspects of it. The best way of tackling this is to list these parties in a methodical way and assess carefully, looking from their viewpoint, what the perceived impact of the project is likely to be and their likely course of action. For example, environmentalists might be concerned that the project is intrusive, destroys views and causes pollution: they can be expected to lobby vigorously in Parliament and perhaps take direct action once construction starts.

In some cases, it may be difficult to forecast the extent of a project's environmental impact. Whereas in the past this might have been left to chance, it will nowadays usually be essential that all aspects be studied in depth, e.g. visual intrusion, use of energy and scarce materials, pollution, noise, destruction of natural environment, effect on nearby amenities, archaeological remains, ease of eventual removal, effect on wildlife.

Such an analysis may suggest courses of action which could keep risk and opposition to a minimum. For example, environmentalists might be invited to participate in the design process, so as to highlight opportunities for reducing the adverse environmental effects. It may even be possible to improve certain aspects of the present environment by slight modifications to the project. Even if it does not prove practicable to go some way to meeting the wishes of environmentalists, the exercise will at the very least give advance warning of the principal grounds on which they are likely to object, so that relevant research can be carried out in advance.

Estimating small probabilities

How can one estimate the probability of occurrence of an extremely unlikely event? If a large number of similar projects have been carried out in the past, past experience is perhaps the best guide. Getting sufficient reliable data of what happened to all those projects might be a significant practical problem, however. If, for example, out of 10 000 bridges, five have collapsed during the past 120 years, the chance of collapse of any new bridge at some point during an assumed life of 120 years can be assessed (other things being equal) as 1 in 2000. In this kind of analysis it is important, however, to get a true correspondence between the number of cases where an event occurs and the number of cases exposed to risk of the event. If the population of 10 000 bridges included some very old ones, and only old bridges had collapsed, the chance of a new bridge collapsing within the next 120 years might be much less than 1 in 2000. On the other hand, if all the five collapses were of relatively new suspension bridges, of which 1000 had been built, then the chance of early collapse of a new suspension bridge

now being built could be as high as 1 in 200.

Differing attitudes to risk

Even if we know precisely what the risk of occurrence of an adverse event will be, and its consequences if it occurs, it is likely that different sponsors might well have different views on whether they are prepared to accept such a risk. For example, a wealthy sponsor might be prepared to take a 10% risk of incurring a significant loss on a project whereas another sponsor, who has lower financial resources, might not. The latter might prefer to have a lower 'expected' return but with more certainty of avoiding a loss. For this reason some sponsors will have a greater desire than others to insure against the risk of loss. Usually a risk will be worth insuring against (or minimising in some other way) if the occurrence of the risk event would cause real difficulty to the sponsoring company or its backers. If the sponsor feels that the consequences of occurrence of the risk event would be comparatively unimportant for him, he will be happy to absorb the risk without having to pay an insurer a profit margin.

Similarly most equity investors, for whom the investment is a small portion of a large portfolio, will be quite happy to accept a downside risk, provided there is sufficient upside potential. They would not normally wish to see costly risk-mitigation action taken if this reduced the 'expected' net present value of the project. For such an investor the losses on some projects are more than balanced out by the gains on others.

Banks which have lent money, on the other hand, cannot usually benefit from the upside potential of a project and their main concern is to avoid downside risks occurring to such an extent that the loan cannot be repaid. They will often be wanting as much risk mitigation to take place as is reasonably practicable, unless there is external security for the loan.

Appendix 2:
Using an investment model

To evaluate any investment, it is necessary to define its objectives, measure these (as far as possible) in financial terms, and then relate the resulting financial parameters to some overall measure of value for the investment over its life (typically, whole-life net present value, as explained below). Generally, the value of an investment is based on the balance of benefits over costs. Typically, the main measures of cost and benefit, stage-by-stage are shown in Table 13.

Benefits and costs are both typically spread over periods of time, as cash flows. It is impossible to conduct anything other than the simplest investment appraisal without building a cash flow model.

Appraisal techniques

There are a number of techniques currently used to appraise projects which are all based on the principle of comparing costs with benefits. Most appraisals are conducted using either a payback period, internal rate of return (IRR) or net present value (NPV). The latter is perhaps the most widely used of the approaches for major projects.

The payback period is simply the number of years of cash flow needed to meet the initial investment. Its simplicity has however to be offset by lack of consideration of the time value of money and of cash flows and risks beyond the payback period. The second method, IRR, overcomes these disadvantages but gives no indication of the amount of value or profit each project will provide. The NPV approach addresses these two latter disadvantages, although it does introduce subjectivity in the requirement to establish a discount rate.

Real or nominal cashflows

Investment appraisals are generally conducted initially on the basis of real costs and revenues, calculated in terms of today's money value. Using nominal cash flows, allowing for future inflation,

Stage	Description	Key financial parameters		Other parameters*
		Benefits	Costs	
1.	Opportunity identification		Cost of study	
2.	Appraisal		Appraisal cost	
3.	Investment planning		Financing cost	
4.	Asset creation		Capital cost	Scope Performance/quality Timing
5.	Operation	Revenue Non-revenue benefits	Operating cost Maintenance cost Renewals cost	
6.	Close-down	Resale/residual value	Decommissioning cost Cost of staff redundancies Disposal cost	

Table 13. Measures of cost and benefit

* These have potential impact on one or more financial parameters

could be confusing at this initial stage because it would produce absolute figures which, particularly in the later years, might be extremely large and hold little relevance in today's terms for such an appraisal. However, adjustments must be made to allow for any costs and benefits which will not escalate approximately in line with future inflation, and these adjustments may need to be based on assumptions about future inflation rates.

Where the project is going to be financially free standing, normally financial models will also be required at a later stage which are based on nominal figures allowing for an assumed rate of inflation in calculating future cash flows. Sensitivity testing using different assumed inflation rates will usually be necessary, in view of the uncertainty in this field. These financial models will also need to allow for any fixed rate funding and the effect of taxation on the economics of the project. Consolidation of accounting statements will also require nominal figures.

It may sometimes happen that a project that appears financially viable using real costs and revenues looks unprofitable once the full financial model is prepared, and vice versa. Even if (as we would recommend) the risk analysis is carried out using real costs and revenues, in order to retain a good 'feel' for all the estimates made in respect of future years, it would still be worth running a preliminary version of the full financial model at a fairly early stage, to prevent abortive work on a project which will not meet investors' financial requirements.

Choice of discount rate

The generally accepted discount rate appropriate to the analysis of public service investments is 6% per annum in real terms. Many commercial firms use discount rates higher than 6%, which serve to reduce the significance of future revenues, and maintenance and operating costs, over the whole life of the asset in comparison with initial construction costs.

This Handbook shows how to link RAMP with an investment model but it does not purport to discuss all aspects of the construction of that investment model or the discount rate to use. In particular the choice of an appropriate discount rate is an important but complex matter which is outside the scope of this Handbook. Ultimately the choice of the discount rate will depend partly on issues such as the company's cost of funds and any hurdle rates that the company sets for its investments. Some companies may wish to use a higher/lower discount rate for projects which they regard as having a higher/lower inherent risk (i.e. a risk which is incapable of mitigation) than for their other projects. If this inherent risk varies significantly over different phases of the project, it may sometimes be appropriate to use different discount rates for each phase.

A high discount rate should not be seen as a substitute for a detailed risk analysis as this could lead to the rejection of profitable low risk projects in favour of more profitable projects that carry unacceptable levels of risk (see Section 1.5). Where the cash flows are based on nominal figures, a higher discount rate will be appropriate than where real cash flows are used.

Actuaries can advise on the choice of a suitable discount rate for the purpose in hand, taking account of the above-mentioned points and developments in modern financial theory in recent years.

Discounting

Discounting is at the heart of the NPV technique. The rationale for discounting is based on the fact that a sum of money now is worth more than at a future time. For example, if we have to forego having £100 in cash for (say) 12 months, then we would need to be paid a sum of interest to cover the loss in value of the money (due to inflation) and the opportunity missed to earn some return by investing the money for a year. Thus if we judge that our losses for waiting a year are 8%, then we are saying that £100 today is equivalent in value to £108 in a year's time. Another way of saying the same thing is that £100 in a year's time is worth £(100 / (100 + 8)) x 100 = £92.59 now. Similarly, £100 pounds in two years' time is now worth £(100 / (100 + 8))(100 / (100 + 8)) x 100, i.e. £(100 / (100 + 8))^2 x 100 = £85.73.

If interest is expressed as a fraction (i.e. 8% = 0.08) then we can restate the above, expressing the net present value of £100 in one year as £(1 / 1.08) x 100 = £92.59. Extending the calculations, Table 14 can be used to calculate the NPV of a cash flow of £100 per year at the end of each of the next three years.

Thus we can express any future cash flow as a net present value by using the above formula and an appropriate interest (or 'discount') rate.

As another example, suppose the total capital cost of a project is £50 million, of which £20 million is spent at the end of year 1 and £30 million at the end of year 2. Then, at a discount rate of 10%, the NPV of the capital cost is: £[(1/1.1) x 20 + (1/1.1)^2 x 30] million = £42.97 million.

Thus each key parameter affecting the value of an investment, whether it is an individual payment or a series of cash flows, can be expressed as a net present value (NPV). Finally, by adding the net present values for benefits and deducting those for costs, an overall whole-life NPV for the investment can be calculated.

A deterministic or stochastic approach

The traditional approach to projecting future cash flows, the deterministic approach, is to consider

each item separately and estimate its most likely value. The next step is to conduct sensitivity tests which typically involve making a pessimistic and optimistic estimate in addition to the most likely. All of the results of the investment appraisal are then presented based on three scenarios; pessimistic, optimistic and the most likely.

The conclusion that can be drawn from such an analysis is necessarily limited. The answer may lie somewhere between the pessimistic and optimistic scenarios and is most likely to be the middle scenario. But how likely is most likely and is optimistic equally as likely as pessimistic? To answer these questions – and others such as what is the probability of a rate of return less than x% or between y% and z% – a stochastic approach may be needed.

A stochastic approach involves fitting statistical distributions to cash flow items instead of making a fixed number of individual estimates. Note that in many situations it may be inappropriate to use continuous risk distributions where insufficient expertise exists. In these instances it may be better to create discrete distributions with only a limited number of outcomes (e.g. 5 or 10). For instance by limiting the outcomes to the most likely, pessimistic and optimistic values and assigning probabilities to each would create a discrete distribution that may in fact represent all the information that is known about the risk.

As a consequence of inputting data into the cash flow model in the form of statistical distributions, the result of the investment appraisal can also be presented as a statistical distribution (see example shown in Figs 13 and 14). Having a distribution of

Years	Future value: £	NPV formula	Value now: £
1	100	(1/1.08) x 100	92.59
2	100	(1/1.08)^2 x 100	85.73
3	100	(1/1.08)^3 x 100	79.38
	NPV		**257.70**

Table 14. Net present value of a cash flow of £100 per year

Real project costs	£ million
Development costs	1.80
Land purchase	2.30
Design work	4.20
Building costs	32.50
Plant and machinery	22.50
Consultant's fees (technical, risk etc)	3.80
Pre-opening costs	4.60
Total costs (current prices)	**71.70**
Key dates	
Construction starts	January 2003
Operations start	April 2005
Major refurbishment	January 2012
Assumptions (margins over RPI)	**p.a.**
Revenue	-0.50%
Operating costs	0.50%
Capital costs — buildings	2.00%
— plant and machinery	1.00%

Figure 13. Typical investment model

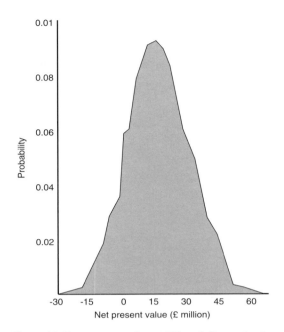

Figure 14. Net present value at 6% real discount rate

NPVs from such an appraisal clearly provides decision makers with the ability to make more informed decisions. It allows an assessment of probability of loss calculations and gives a better insight into the sensitivity of the project to adverse conditions.

This stochastic approach has to be used with discretion. Correlation should be allowed for; thus it would be inappropriate to ignore the fact that there is a linkage between short term interest rates and inflation. The number of cash flow items expressed as a statistical distribution should also be limited in order to make the process more realistic and manageable.

The decision on whether to use the stochastic or deterministic approach depends on the scope of the investment appraisal. Clearly, the level of sophistication required and the information that is likely to be available will determine the approach to be adopted. A stochastic approach is therefore only likely to be appropriate for medium to large projects.

Scenario analysis is a useful practical alternative to a full stochastic approach (see Section 9.2 of main text). It is likely to be worthwhile to carry out scenario analysis before embarking on a stochastic model, because the former is much less expensive and can often give a sufficient 'feel' of the risks for the purpose in hand. Moreover, scenario analysis helps to avoid the danger, inherent in stochastic modelling, of losing sight of the key assumptions on which the results depend.

Accuracy

Even a simple model has to be correct. The nature of cash flow models is that small mistakes can have significant consequences, particularly for marginal projects. It is essential that models are documented and independently audited both for structure and accuracy of input. Equally important is the reasonableness of the cash flows. Clearly, they are only estimates but they should be checked by a third party where possible. Allowance must be made in the cash flows for all the 'knock on' effects arising from the project in respect of the sponsor's central costs or other activities.

Appendix 3: A RAMP risk matrix

Figure 15. RAMP risk matrix

Cause of risk

Legend – cause codes:

- **1. Political:** a) Government, b) Public opinion, c) Environmental change, d) Legislation, e) Wars, terrorism, riots, f) Poor public relations, g) Crime
- **2. Business:** a) Demand failure, b) Competition, c) Premature obsolescence, d) Safety standards
- **3. Economic:** a) Cost inflation/interest rates, b) Currency fluctuations, c) Extreme economic conditions
- **4. Project:** a) Lack of definition, b) Technical innovation, c) Lack of leadership, d) Lack of technical competence, e) Lack of commitment, f) Poor planning and control, g) Inadequate legal framework, h) Inadequate resourcing of project, i) Inadequate progress on project, j) Labour relations, k) Human error or incompetence
- **5. Natural:** a) Bad weather, b) Earthquake/volcanic eruption, c) Fire or explosion, d) Adverse ground conditions
- **6. Financial:** a) Inadequate financial margins, b) Unbalanced sharing of risk

Investment stage/risk event	1a	1b	1c	1d	1e	1f	1g	2a	2b	2c	2d	3a	3b	3c	4a	4b	4c	4d	4e	4f	4g	4h	4i	4j	4k	5a	5b	5c	5d	6a	6b
1. Opportunity identification } no significant risks																															
2. Appraisal																															
3. Investment planning and preparation																															
Promotion of concept																															
loss of intellectual property rights							x																	x	x						
claims for infringement of intellectual property rights							x														x			x	x						
Design																															
non compliant design (failure to meet specified standards)															x			x	x										x		
design based on inadequate site investigation data															x			x		x									x		
professional negligence							x								x			x		x	x	x							x		
Contract negotiations																															
failure to agree development framework with client															x		x		x				x							x	x
failure to resolve conflicts of interest within promoting consortium															x		x		x				x							x	x
contractual terms and conditions worse than expected																							x							x	x
Project approval																															
failure to obtain approval/consents	x	x															x		x												
long delay before approval granted	x	x		x																							x				
unforeseen modifications to project			x												x	x				x							x				
cost of obtaining approval higher than expected	x	x		x																x											
inclusion of contingent liabilities (e.g. environmental clean up)	x	x												x																	
introduction of regulatory controls (fares, competition policy)	x		x	x				x																							
4. Asset creation																															
Raising of capital																															
capital requirements increased by inflation												x	x	x																	
interest costs higher than expected												x	x	x																	
capital not available due to market conditions														x																	
capital not available due to poor market perceptions of project			x																											x	x
capital not available due to withdrawal of support by key organisations			x						x										x	x			x							x	x
refinancing not available or terms worse than expected			x						x					x					x	x			x							x	x
default due to insufficient project revenue								x	x					x																x	x
default due to external factors			x	x	x			x						x																	
Construction																															
inability to obtain land, access right, wayleaves			x																												
compensation costs higher than expected	x	x		x	x																										
delays due to *force majeure*			x																							x	x	x	x		
delays due to other causes			x		x														x	x		x	x	x		x	x				
cost over-runs												x						x	x	x		x	x	x		x	x	x	x		
insolvency of promoter																														x	
insolvency of contractor																														x	
third party damages																				x							x				
failure of project to gain technical acceptance			x												x	x		x		x	x										
structural failure post completion							x								x			x													
5. Operation																															
Expenses and maintenance																															
unforeseen operating costs			x	x						x	x	x						x		x			x								
major repairs				x							x	x						x									x	x			
third party claims																				x							x				
accident damage																				x								x			
Revenue																															
operating volume less than expected			x		x			x	x	x						x															
unit revenues lower than expected				x				x	x							x															
unforeseen competition			x	x					x																						
revenue collection costs higher than expected											x				x																
revenues negotiable (influence of large customers)									x																						
loss of revenue due to late completion or temporary closure																											x		x		
revenue insufficient to cover debt servicing								x																							x
revenue loss due to fraud			x				x																x								
6. Close-down																															
lifetime below expectations			x	x				x	x	x	x																x	x	x		
residual value less than expected		x	x									x	x																		
dismantling costs higher than expected	x		x																	x		x					x	x			

Appendix 4:
Risk assessment tables

This Appendix describes a very simple technique which is designed to assist in the prioritisation of risks for analysis (see Section 4.3 of main text). The idea is that each risk event is first of all classified into one of several 'likelihood' categories, according to its probability of occurrence, and is then classified into one of several 'consequence' categories, according to the severity of the consequences if the risk event occurs. Each category has a score and the score for likelihood is multiplied by the score for consequence to get the combined score for the risk event. The risk events with the highest combined score are then selected for priority analysis.

Set out below are some specimen risk assessment tables. However, it should be emphasised that there is a variety of ways in which such tables can be drawn up, so as to meet the needs of the particular project, with different categories and differing

decision rules about which risks should be eliminated, managed or ignored.

To explain the use of the specimen tables, suppose that a particular risk event has a 30% chance of occurring at least once during the project's life cycle. If it occurs, it will be a serious threat to the investment. It will be awarded a score of 8 in Table 15 and a score of 100 in Table 16, leading to a combined score of 800 (see Table 17). According to the suggested decision rule, this risk event would come into the category of undesirable, i.e. a risk which one should attempt to avoid or transfer if at all possible.

Suppose, however, that the same risk event had been assessed as having a disastrous consequence if it occurs. Then the combined score would have been 8 000, which means it is an intolerable risk. If it cannot be eliminated, transferred or avoided, the whole future of the project may be in doubt.

Description	Scenario	Probability	Scale value
Highly likely	Very frequent occurrence	Over 85%	16
Likely	More than evens chance	50–85%	12
Fairly likely	Quite often occurs	21–49%	8
Unlikely	Small likelihood but could well happen	1–20%	4
Very unlikely	Not expected to happen	Less than 1%	2
Extremely unlikely	Just possible but very surprising	Less than 0.01%	1

Table 15. Risk assessment table – likelihood. This table categorises risks according to their probability of occurring at least once at some point during the whole project life-cycle.

Description	Scenario	Scale value
Disastrous	Business investment could not be sustained (e.g. deaths, bankruptcy)	1000
Severe	Serious threat to business or investment	100
Substantial	Reduces profit significantly	20
Marginal	Small effect on profit	3
Negligible	Trivial effect on profit	1

Table 16. Risk assessment table – consequence

Likelihood		Consequence				
		Disastrous (1000)	Severe (100)	Substantial (20)	Marginal (3)	Negligible (1)
Highly likely	(16)	16 000	1600	320	48	16
Likely	(12)	12 000	1200	240	36	12
Fairly likely	(8)	8000	800	160	24	8
Unlikely	(4)	4000	400	80	12	4
Very unlikely	(2)	2000	200	40	6	2
Extremely unlikely	(1)	1000	100	20	3	1

Table 17. Risk assessment table – acceptance of risk

Points	Category	Action required
Over 1000	Intolerable	Must eliminate or transfer risk
101–1000	Undesirable	Attempt to avoid or transfer risk
21–100	Acceptable	Retain and manage risk
Up to 20	Negligible	Can be ignored

Key to acceptance of risk

Appendix 5: Insuring risk

Introduction

While traditional insurance markets exist for specific established exposures, the insurance industry is starting to innovate successfully by devising new flexible forms of cover which meet the need for an integrated and holistic approach to the insurance of project risks. Emphasis is beginning to shift from the mechanical placement of insurance for single risks, which has hitherto been the traditional approach, to the devising of an optimal outcome for a package of risks over the lifetime of a project.

Projects coming under the Private Finance Initiative (and derivative programmes like Public Private Partnerships) typically demand a broader and more flexible stance from insurers in tackling the umbrella of risks within a project, and insurance markets have been able to respond to this demand. As insurance markets become increasingly familiar with the type of risks covered, the scope for continued innovation to the benefit of the client will grow.

Common risk categories

While all projects are different, common categories of risk for major projects include

- loss of assets during and after construction
- unforeseen ground conditions
- loss of income stream due to delay in construction completion
- insufficiency of revenue stream (e.g. due to erroneous forecasting)
- liability to third parties
- design liabilities
- liability to employees
- failure of information technology.

Methods of insurance

Insurance is usually arranged in relation to a particular phase of the project and the following describes some of the ways that large projects are insured.

The construction phase

Construction all risks (CAR): Insurance against physical loss or damage of assets used during construction, including the contract and temporary works, mechanical and electrical equipment, construction plant and equipment, and any existing buildings or structures to be retained.

Third party (public) liability: Indemnity if there is legal liability to third parties for physical injury or damage to property. Extension of cover to provide insurance for pure financial loss and for design faults is being considered.

Professional indemnity: Legal liability caused by negligence in carrying out 'professional' duties for third parties. This must be considered alongside the contractual structure, the liabilities of the parties within the project and third party liability insurance.

Employer's liability: An indemnity which covers the employer against legal liability if employees suffer physical injury or disease while in their employ.

Advance loss of profit: Cover if revenue from a project is interrupted because of delays caused by physical loss or damage insured under a CAR policy. Cover is provided for a range of financial losses such as debt servicing through to remuneration of full gross profits (income less cost savings). The individual exposures of all participants in the project need to be considered.

The operational phase

Material damage: Cover against loss or damage to the physical assets of the project. Areas of cover that need to be addressed include whether to include mechanical and electrical breakdown; whether cover should be against all risks or only for specified perils; whether cover should be 'as new' or should reflect asset depreciation.

Business interruption: Interruption to the revenue stream caused by physical loss or damage. Cover can range from the cost of servicing debt through to gross profits foregone. Cover can be extended to include denial of access, utility failure and other risks.

Latent defects: Cover for structural damage, imminent threat of collapse or failure of the weather proofing envelope – including consequential loss – arising from a latent defect in construction which manifests itself in the first twelve years after construction.

Third party (public) liability: Legal liability to third parties for personal injury (including disease) and damage. Pure financial loss extension should be considered.

Employer's liability: Legal liability for injury to employees. The TUPE regulations should be considered in relation to questions of liability for employees of acquired businesses.

Motor: Damage to owned vehicles, or those leased or hired to the project, together with associated liability to third parties.

Directors and officers liability: The legal liability of directors and officers of the project arising from their managerial position.

Others – specific to the project: Depending on the circumstances of the project, other coverages, such as medical malpractice liability, key-man insurance, etc., need to be considered.

Extending the risk management strategy

Apart from obvious legislative limitations and restrictions incorporated into the process, the scope for creative solutions increases as we move away from the working layer (attritional losses), and as risks are combined and the terms extended. One of the most important aims in combining risks over a period of time would be to take a more strategic perspective on the handling of risk and achieve longer term objectives – such as, the smoothing of the premium levels and the achievement of cash flow stability, as well as building long-term strategic alliances with insurers.

Another key driver to what strategy is adopted is the probable size of projects and exposures, and whether it is likely that traditional insurance markets will find it difficult to absorb the risk. Traditional insurance may exist, but at a price that is not economic. A commercial view may be needed on whether insurance represents value for the risk which is being transferred. When considering whether to insure risks that they have not previously insured, insurers are likely to be much more receptive if relevant statistics of the frequency and severity of the risks concerned are available from past experience.

Insurance markets available

As well as pre-existing insurance markets, new markets may need to be created and early involvement by insurers and risk experts in establishing these is critically important, especially if projects are very large. The availability of insurance is likely to depend on the availability of data and knowledge of the risks (and familiarity of the insurance markets with the risks). The aim is to design a customised solution package that will give the broadest cover at the most economic price possible, using an optimal combination of financial markets.

Limited risk transfer

Below are summarised a number of ways in which risk can be transferred to a limited extent, which can be useful where full insurance cover cannot be obtained.

- *Unfunded self-insurance:* whereby the owner would simply pay losses as and when they arise from cashflow.
- *Pre-funded self-insurance:* in which cash is set aside for this purpose in a stable financial asset.
- *Owned captive:* a limited purpose insurance company specially formed to insure or re-insure the risks of its parent company.
- *Rent a captive:* this is a funding vehicle owned by a third party which operates as an insurance company for a limited number of participants.
- *Mutual:* an insurance company owned jointly by a group of entities, all of which have homogeneous exposures to risk, such as the partners in a consortium.
- *Post loss funding:* funding of losses by borrowing from equity or debt markets, etc.
- *Financial insurance/reinsurance products:* use of insurance policies to fund risk exposures.
- *Insurance derivative products:* the principle of these products is similar to financial derivatives.

Acknowledgement
The working party is indebted to Aon Risk Consultants for kindly supplying a paper on which this Appendix is largely based.

Appendix 6: Mitigation and control of risks in computer projects – some suggestions

For large computer projects the following suggestions are offered for risk mitigation:

- establish the objectives very clearly and comprehensively at the outset;
- identify the lead sponsor, if more than one sponsor is involved, and set up a clear machinery for decision-making by the sponsors;
- subdivide the project into semi-independent modules;
- use established software which is already working, as far as possible (even if there is some loss of functionality), reserving any brand-new software to a relatively small part of the whole;
- avoid as far as possible any technologies which have not previously been tested thoroughly in practice;
- check carefully that the project, if delivered according to specification, will in fact fully achieve the objectives;
- ensure there is clear ownership of the project at an appropriately senior level;
- revisit the project specification to see if further modifications can be made to reduce the risks which have been identified;
- define clearly which risks will be borne by the contractor and which by the sponsor(s), and write the contract accordingly (with an appropriately structured payment mechanism if it is a PFI contract);
- take up references regarding contractors' performance on previous projects;
- choose a contractor with a record for reliable delivery, even if not lowest cost;
- give appropriate financial incentives (or penalties) to the contractor to ensure maximum effort on his part to control risks;
- set up well-defined mechanisms to control specification changes, with appropriate levels of authorisation;
- use a flexible design that can readily be adapted to cope with legislative changes, and establish an early warning system that flags adverse consequences of legislative changes in time;
- ensure that the development team has sufficiently high-quality 'back up cover' in case some members fall sick or leave;
- consider whether insurance could play a part (e.g. key-man insurance);
- establish contingency plans to extend the life of the current system should there be a time over-run on the new project;
- set up a system for testing in modules the parts of the system which involve new software or new technology, with contingency plans for dealing with the situation should they not work;
- establish contingency plans in case the contractor goes out of business while the project is being developed or under warranty;
- plan in detail the transition from the old system to the new.

Once the project is authorised, it is vital that proper machinery should be put in place to control the residual risks, including:

- appointment of a fully competent project manager with a clear remit and defined authority;
- preparation of containment and contingency plans;
- appointment of risk custodians;
- appropriate budgetary controls, including contingency allowances for minor variations;
- strict controls on even minor specification changes;
- controls to make sure that all the intended risk mitigation actions are in fact taken;
- a crisis management committee that can be called at short notice;
- establishment of project 'landmarks' at the outset, with dates attached to them – some of these landmarks will be followed by additional gateways requiring reaffirmation of project continuance;
- a detailed procedure for monitoring and analysing trends;
- full communication to all concerned;
- regular risk reviews including reviews of whether the project (when completed) will still meet customers' needs if these have changed;
- a project steering group, meeting monthly, to consider emerging issues of policy, timing or resource constraints; all interested parties should be represented, at a sufficiently senior level, and the project manager should attend.

Appendix 7: A simple RAMP appraisal process

Introduction

This Appendix presents a simple process for appraising competing projects and choosing between them, using RAMP methodology for risk assessment, combined with a suitable investment model. A practical example of the process is given, together with a method for deciding whether risk mitigation is financially worthwhile or not.

Process summary

It will be assumed here that the company's weighted-average cost of capital is 6% p.a. plus price inflation. (A different rate can, of course, be used if appropriate.) The process of appraisal for each project may be summarised as follows:

(a) Determine the objective(s), scope and requirements of the project and work out the project plan, at least in outline.

(b) Carefully evaluate the cash flows each year into the future, on the basis of no inflation, assuming that the most likely scenario for the project occurs.

(c) Discount these cash flows to the present time using a discount rate of 6% p.a., to get the Net Present Value (NPV) of the project.

(d) Construct alternative scenarios and repeat steps (b) and (c) above.

(e) Attach probabilities to each scenario and hence obtain a probability distribution of the NPVs. Also weight the resulting NPVs by the probabilities to obtain a weighted-average NPV.

(f) Consider risk mitigation and amend the probability distribution of the NPVs (and the weighted-average NPV) to allow for the risk mitigation measures which are to be adopted.

Once the calculations have been completed, a decision can be made on which of the projects has the most attractive probability distribution of NPVs. This will not necessarily be the project with the highest expected NPV, if that project has a substantial downside risk.

We shall now consider each of the above steps in more detail.

Determination of objective(s) and plan

The first and most crucial step is to determine the objective(s) of the project. This should not be done lightly but needs careful consideration so as to make sure that all the vital objectives are captured. For example, the objectives of a new railway will not be merely to transport passengers and freight and make a profit but also to do so safely. The scope and requirements of the project will need thought, including such matters as whether to build in spare capacity, the degree of flexibility required, and the safety considerations once it is operational. The next step will be to work out the project plan, at least in outline: how will it be done, how long will it take, how much business can be expected etc?

Evaluation of cash flows

Even at a preliminary stage it is essential to evaluate the forecast cash flows properly, with as much accuracy as possible, and taking account of 'knock on' effects. Mistakes or carelessness here could lead to incorrect investment decisions. Forecasts should where possible be reality-checked against comparable projects. Consideration should be given to whether the effect (if any) of the project on the sponsor's tax position needs to be taken into account as a cash flow. Throughout this Appendix cash outflows will be taken as negative and cash inflows as positive. Most projects will commence with negative cash flows at the outset, as capital is invested, and will then start to receive positive cash flows once the asset being constructed has become operational.

Discounting the cash flows

A useful simplifying assumption is that cash flows take place half-way through the year to which they relate. In the initial years when capital is being invested this assumption may be wide of the mark, but the effect on the NPVs is likely to be so small that it can be ignored at the initial stages of the work. We shall discount all the cash flows to a point six months after the commencement of the investment, i.e. half-way through the first year. Hence we shall assume that the expenditure incurred in the first year of the project does not need to be discounted at all and that the revenue earned in (say) the fourth year of the project is discounted for exactly three years. (For the chosen project a more accurate discounting calculation can be made as a check before the final decision is made to go ahead.)

Consider an example of a computer software project which is expected to take one year to design and implement and which will then result in net cost savings for four years. The cash flows for the most likely scenario are expressed in terms of present day prices (£000s) with no allowance for future inflation:

Year	Cash flow £000s
1	− 1000
2	+ 300
3	+ 400
4	+ 400
5	+ 400
	+ 500

NPV

$$= -1000 + 300/1.06 + 400/1.06^2 + 400/1.06^3 + 400/1.06^4$$

$$= -1000 + 283 + 356 + 336 + 317$$

$$= 292$$

Thus the project can be expected to earn a future flow of profits after allowing for the cost of capital, equivalent to a lump sum of £292 000 at the outset. This assumes, of course, that things go according to plan.

Construction of alternative scenarios

The next step is to identify and analyse the major risks in the project, paying particular attention to the underlying causes. A risk is 'major' if its consequences would be serious, even if it is unlikely to occur. Ways of identifying risk include:

- check-lists of problems from previous similar investments, other case studies, technical papers, safety reviews and environmental impact studies;
- site visits;
- review of baseline plans, other key documents and outline designs;
- brainstorming sessions.

A list of commonly found risks is set out at the end of this Appendix, but this list is not exhaustive.

For each risk event, the consequence if it occurs must next be identified. The results are entered up in a risk register for the project. Upside potential as well as downside risk must be identified and analysed. Any assumptions which have been made in identifying or analysing the risks should also be recorded.

Some alternative scenarios for the project will then be constructed, having regard to the risks which have been analysed. This is a matter for judgement, where one is sometimes trying to

capture, in only a very small number of scenarios, a wide range of risks. A useful way of constructing a scenario is to select the mid-point of a possible range of variation. Thus, for example, if there could be a cost increase, should a specified risk event occur, of between £200 and £400, the scenario would take £300 as the mid-point. Some risks can be grouped, at least at this early stage of the analysis.

Let us assume that, for the computer project given as an example in 'Discounting the cash flows', the risk analysis leads to the identification of the following major alternative scenarios:

Scenario	Type of risk	Risk event	Probability of occurrence	Expected impact on project
A	Expected	None	55%	None
B	Upside	As A and system know-how can be sold to other organisations	10%	Revenue £200 000 more in year 2
C	Downside	Technological delay	15%	System takes extra year and cost increased by £300 000
D	Downside	System does not work well	10%	Savings reduced by £100 000 each year
E	Downside	Technological delay and system does not work well	10%	As in scenarios C and D

Obtaining a Probability Distribution of NPVs.

7. Then we have the following analysis:

	Scenario				
Year	A £000	B £000	C £000	D £000	E £000
1	−1000	−1000	−1000	−1000	−1000
2	300	500	−300	200	−300
3	400	400	300	300	200
4	400	400	400	300	300
5	400	400	400	300	300
6	–	–	400	–	300
Net cash flows	500	700	200	100	−200
NPV	292	481	−64	−54	−391
Probability of occurrence	55%	10%	15%	10%	10%
Expected (weighted average) NPV = 155					

Hence on 65% of occasions such a project would show a profit but on 35% of occasions it would show a loss. The loss could be as high as £391 000 but might be even more, remembering that scenario E is a mid-point of a range of possible outcomes. On average a large number of such projects would show a capitalised profit (after taking account of interest costs) of £155 000 each.

Risk mitigation

Let us suppose that the external contractor who will carry out the work is prepared to bear the whole of any extra software development costs (as in scenarios C and E), provided that the contract price is increased by £80 000. Is it worthwhile for the sponsor to accept this offer?

We can evaluate the various scenarios again, assuming that this new condition applies, as in the table below.

The project will now show a profit on 80% of occasions and a loss on only 20%. Moreover, the 'maximum' (mid-point) loss is reduced from £391 000 to £188 000. This risk profile may well be more

attractive than the original one to a sponsor who would find losses hard to bear. On the other hand, for a large sponsor where the project is one among many projects, the better expected NPV of the original situation (£155 000 instead of £145 000) would suggest that the risk should remain unmitigated.

Further work for the chosen project

The method can, of course, be adapted as necessary. A higher degree of analysis would be appropriate for a very large project, for example, and this might involve stochastic modelling once a rough 'fix' had been made by scenario analysis. Moreover, a much more careful application of RAMP methodology is desirable for the selected project (even for a project of quite a small size and cost), since this will help in:
* identifying further risk mitigation options;
* controlling the residual risk remaining after some of the risks have been mitigated.

Particular attention should be paid to any 'disaster' risks, to see if they can be mitigated at a reasonable cost. Any assumptions which have

Scenario					
Year	A £000	B £000	C £000	D £000	E £000
1	−1080	−1080	−1080	−1080	−1080
2	300	500	–	200	–
3	400	400	300	300	200
4	400	400	400	300	300
5	400	400	400	300	300
6	–	–	400	–	300
Net cash flows	420	620	420	20	20
NPV	212	401	139	−134	−188
Probability of occurrence	55%	10%	15%	10%	10%
Expected (weighted average) NPV = 145					

been made at an earlier stage should be rechecked to see if they are reasonable. Sensitivity testing should be undertaken, to see what would be the result of varying key assumptions. (For example, in the above-mentioned computer project, it was assumed that four years' worth of benefits would be obtained – but suppose the system became prematurely obsolete and only three years' worth of benefits were achieved before a better system came into operation? Or what would be the effect of altering the assumed probabilities of the different scenarios?)

Conclusion

The process outlined in this Appendix depends for its success on the input of good quality data and carefully calculated cash flows. It also needs the exercise of good judgement in the construction of appropriate risk scenarios. Every project has its 'champion' and it is important to avoid bias, whether intentional or unintentional, when obtaining data from such a person. Appraisals should preferably be carried out by people who can take an objective view of the various factors.

Only an outline of the process can be given here, to indicate the way in which project appraisal can incorporate RAMP risk analysis in a simple and practical way. Actuaries can help firms and public bodies to draw up procedures and methods to adapt the process to their own particular needs.

SOME COMMONLY FOUND RISKS

Some of the areas where risks often exist in projects are:
- Insufficiently defined objectives
- Design problems
- Incorrect or biased cashflow estimates
- Suppression of key information
- Capital cost
- Usage and revenue
- Running cost
- Time taken to become operational
- Efficiency level once operational
- Premature deterioration
- Premature obsolescence
- Competition (including new players)
- *Force majeure*
- Fraud/crime
- Political developments
- New laws on environment, trade restrictions, higher taxes, etc.
- Planning permission
- Opposition from third parties
- Safety hazards
- Unproven construction methods or leading-edge technology
- Loss of key personnel
- Insolvency of contractor
- Disagreement among a group of sponsors
- Hidden, unstated or untested assumptions
- Obtaining finance
- Danger from need to refinance later
- Increased cost due to interest rate or exchange rate changes
- Decommissioning when project life is over
- Economic downturns

Appendix 8: Applying RAMP to a large project – a case study

Introduction

The RAMP process is to be used to support the decision to invest in and then to monitor the following (hypothetical) project. It is proposed that a tolled road bridge should be built across a river estuary which is at present served only by car ferries. Two large towns A and B are separated by the river. The new bridge will reduce their distance by road from the present 120 miles (using a bridge further up river) to only 20 miles. Most road traffic between A and B uses the car ferries and the overall journey time is about 60 minutes at present. This will be reduced to about 25 minutes once the new bridge has been built.

Alternative sites

There are three possible sites for the new bridge. Option 1 involves tunnelling through a hill for the access road, with consequent expense and risk. Option 2 does not involve tunnelling and is in many ways ideal, except that it would involve the destruction of a historic castle and some ancient woodlands and sites of special scientific interest. Option 3 would use a site much further down the estuary. Although this would necessitate a longer bridge, the approach roads would cross greenfield sites and the overall cost of construction would be less than under Options 1 or 2. The principal problem with Option 3 is that the site can be windy and on 20 days a year high sided lorries would have to be banned.

Traffic forecasts

At present 5000 cars and 1000 lorries a day use the ferries. The toll is 60p per car and £3 per lorry, so the overall gross revenue for the ferry operator is £6000 per day. Both A and B are expanding rapidly and it is thought that the new bridge will stimulate further traffic growth because of the reduced journey time.

The new bridge will take five years to plan and construct and it is estimated that after it has been in operation for five years (i.e. ten years from the outset) the total traffic volume on the bridge will be about 15 000 cars and 3000 lorries per day. The ferries will remain in operation but it is estimated that they will attract only one-tenth as much traffic as the bridge. The bridge is assumed to have an operating life of at least fifty years. Operating expenses are estimated at £0.8 million per annum.

Preliminary appraisal

The preliminary appraisal of the project proceeds by making some simple discounted cash flow calculations, using the present ferry tolls. These calculations suggest that the project may be viable on Options 2 and 3, but probably not viable from a financial viewpoint on Option 1 unless the tolls are raised. (See the Annex to this Appendix for illustrative calculations relating to this and subsequent stages of the appraisal.)

Preliminary risk assessment

A high-level preliminary risk analysis is made, from which it is concluded that there is a significant risk, if Option 2 is adopted, that there will be a long delay and that the bridge will probably not get planning permission because of opposition from conservationists. Therefore Option 2 is rejected.

Second risk assessment

At this point the team concerned with the project holds a brainstorming session to identify the risks involved in the remaining options. They produce the following list:

- planning consent denied
- towns A and B do not expand as fast as expected
- fire, hurricane, earthquake, terrorist activity
- more efficient ferry service introduced
- Option 1 tunnel collapses
- discovery of archaeological remains delays construction
- maintenance costs higher than expected
- capital cost overrun
- ferry company reduces prices and takes more traffic
- petrol tax is raised
- bridge collapses due to faulty design or assembly
- heavy repairs needed
- ship collides with bridge.

Desk-top analysis

Further study produces the following additional list of risks

- tolls prohibited by new legislation
- nationalisation of bridge companies
- weather pattern changes, so bridge available for less time per year
- tolls diverted through fraud
- premature obsolescence.

Evaluation

For each of these risks a preliminary assessment is made of the probability of occurrence, the impact on the project finances, and an assessment of how the risk in question can be managed. Scenarios involving 'upside' are also considered, for example, the possibility that more traffic may use the bridge than anticipated. For each scenario (whether upwards or downwards) the financial effect on the project return is calculated, assuming that the event in question occurs.

Review stage

The project team then reviews the work which has been done to date. Ideas are generated for possible modifications to the project, in order to reduce some of the risk areas or improve the likely rate of financial return. A further brainstorming session is held, which develops the following list of possibilities:

- raise toll levels
- strengthen the bridge at extra cost
- construct a service area at one end of the bridge
- buy up the ferry company and its fixed assets
- re-examine whether there is an alternative site not previously identified
- allow advertising on or near the bridge
- build windshields to increase the availability of the bridge on windy days
- build a tunnel instead of a bridge.

A decision is now taken on whether it is worth proceeding to the later stages of the analysis.

Model building

At this stage a simple mathematical model is built, based on the experiences of similar projects elsewhere, to show the effect on costs and revenues of a number of alternative scenarios. One of the key tasks is to model the traffic flow across the bridge in the event of the ferry company offering various levels of service and charges and with the tolls for the bridge being set at alternative levels. Another task is to refine the probability estimates for the various scenarios, carrying out research where necessary on the experience of similar completed projects elsewhere. After appropriate testing the model is used to re-run the analyses referred to above with a greater level of confidence.

Planning of risk mitigation

For each of the risk areas identified, consideration is given to possible mitigation options, based on the brainstorming discussions and consideration by experts, with the results shown below.

In the light of this analysis, some preliminary investigations are made into the possibility of acquiring the ferry company and its assets. Professional advice provides an estimate of the likely price and a judgement is made (supported by the mathematical model) that the

bridge toll could be at least 10% higher if the ferry tolls were controlled. Some simple discounted cash flow calculations suggest that the overall project would be financially viable. It is therefore decided that the project will now have two principal activities – building and operating the bridge and also buying the ferry company, with a view to controlling its activities and tolls.

Third risk assessment

A further brainstorming session is held to identify

Risk mitigation options

Risk	Likelihood	Impact	Chosen action
Planning consent denied	low	very high	discuss with planners at early stage
Towns A and B do not expand at expected rate	low	high	none
Fire, hurricane, earthquake or terrorist activity	low	high	insure
More efficient ferry service	low	high	buy ferry company
Tunnel collapses	low	high	use proven methods and quality contractors
Discovery of archaeological remains	low	medium	add contingency plan and budget
Higher maintenance costs than expected	high	low	none
Capital cost overrun	high	low	obtain fixed price contract
Ferry company reduces prices to take more traffic	medium	high	buy ferry company
Petrol tax imposed, resulting in reduced traffic	low	low	none
Bridge collapses	low	very high	impose quality regime, and incentivise designers and contractors
Heavy repairs needed	low	medium	impose quality regime, and incentivise designers and contractors
Ship collides with bridge	low	medium	work with harbour authority and design for high visibility
Tolls prohibited by new legislation	low	very high	none
Nationalisation of bridge company	low	high	none
Weather more severe, limits availability	low	medium	insure
Tolls diverted through fraud	medium	medium	insure with fidelity bonds/improve financial management
Premature obsolescence	low	medium	design-in maximum flexibility

the additional risk areas from the proposed ferry company acquisition, with the following results

- acquisition proves more costly than anticipated
- acquisition proves impossible after substantial costs incurred
- government rules that resulting monopoly of crossing would be unacceptable
- ferry company has hidden liabilities e.g. for quay maintenance
- ferry company pension fund proves to have a deficit
- competing hovercraft service introduced by a third party
- unexpectedly heavy capital expenditure on ferries required in next five years before bridge opens
- ferry staff strike in protest at bridge plans
- ferry disaster results in lawsuits
- new EU regulations increase costs of ferry operations.

Further risk-mitigation exercise

Each of the additional risk areas is considered in depth, with a view to identifying how the risk can be mitigated or eliminated. This is an important step (analogous to the consideration given to possible mitigation options in Table 23). The conclusion is reached that the additional risks can be mitigated sufficiently and that the scope of the project does not need to be enlarged further.

Finance

The next stage is to consider how the project might be financed. Since there remain a number of risks where no action can be taken to manage them, the project will need to be financed at least partly by investors who are prepared to absorb these risks, e.g. equity shareholders. On the other hand part of the necessary finance might well be obtainable from banks and bondholders, if they judge that the residual risks, after the mitigation actions outlined above, are

sufficiently low as not to be likely to jeopardise the interest payments and the eventual repayment of the sum lent. Discussions need to take place with the merchant banks who will be aware of the terms which prospective investors and lenders are likely to accept. The RAMP report itself may be a useful document for the purpose of demonstrating to investors and lenders the following critical points

- that the risks have been properly identified and evaluated
- that the risks have been mitigated as far as possible
- that the residual risks are clearly identified and quantified.

Preparation of the submission

A formal RAMP report is prepared, describing in some detail the results obtained from the analysis. This is accompanied by a recommendation for the decision-makers on whether to proceed and, if so, whether Option 1 or Option 3 should be adopted. The report also

- identifies the key risks and shows how it is planned to mitigate at least some of them
- presents a discounted cash flow calculation showing the expected financial outcome and the extent to which this is likely to vary in practice – some sophisticated computer-based simulations of possible outcomes, and their likely probabilities, may lie behind this calculation
- identifies how the project is to be financed and the degree of commitment which has been obtained
- describes how the project will be monitored during the construction period and the initial operation.

Decision

For a major project like this the decision-makers will need to understand the project and its risks and rewards intimately. Not only will they read the submission very carefully but they will talk to members of the project team and as many of the key players as possible, such as leaders of the local community, politicians, civil servants etc. They may wish to obtain an independent view on the project from an external consultant. They will certainly wish to consider carefully any scenarios which could have a severe adverse effect on the project's financial outcome, even where the probability of such scenarios occurring is considered small. Finally the decision-makers will bring to bear their own experience, intuition and judgement, paying special regard to any relevant environmental or political considerations, and any known bias among the members of the project team.

The interests of any groups adversely affected by the project will need to be weighed carefully in the balance. A decision will be needed on which of the alternative options for the project should be adopted. A competent project management team will need to be appointed.

Monitoring arrangements

Detailed plans for controlling the remaining risks will be drawn up and approved. Appropriate monitoring arrangements will be established, with formal RAMP reviews planned to be carried out at intervals or when major unexpected developments occur. The key risk areas envisaged will have been identified at the outset but the effect on the project's viability of any changes in the level of risk should be considered carefully. The periodic reviews should also consider other risk areas which may have come to light subsequently. The computer based simulations will need to be updated and revisions to the financial projections prepared. A major purpose of the reviews will be to identify options for improving the eventual financial outcome or reducing the risks still further in the light of new developments. Particular attention will be paid to whether 'milestone events' identified in the risk

mitigation plan have been achieved to time, and to the outlook for the achievement of future milestones. The results of the reviews, and recommendations on any major decisions required, will be communicated to the senior decision-making level.

Conclusion

The main points that this case study illustrates are summarised in Section 9.2.

Annex: The investment model

This Annex gives an indication of how the NPV calculations would proceed for the above bridge case study. However, the work is taken only to a very elementary level, to illustrate the principles involved. It will be assumed that the NPVs are calculated at a discount rate of 6% p.a. and that tax is ignored.

The assumed cash flows are shown in Table 18 (on a 'most likely' basis) for each of the three options identified in the case study.

The cash flows shown in Table 18 and their NPVs are summarised in Table 19.

Sensitivity calculations are then performed based on
- slightly optimistic values, i.e
  — revenues 10% higher
  — operating costs 25% lower
  — capital costs 5% lower
- most likely values
- slightly pessimistic values, i.e.
  — revenues 10% lower
  — operating costs 25% higher
  — capital costs 5% higher

The results are illustrated in Table 20.

The results suggest that the project may be profitable but that the risks involved could produce a loss.

The scenario method of analysing risks, for Option 3 only, is illustrated in Table 21.

The sub-scenarios in Table 21 may be combined into twelve scenarios, as shown in Table 22.

Phase	Year	Option 1: £ million	Option 2: £ million	Option 3: £ million
Planning and construction	1	−10.0	−8.0	−8.0
	2	−15.0	−14.0	−13.0
	3	−15.0	−14.0	−13.0
	4	−20.0	−16.0	−16.0
	5	−8.0	−10.0	−8.0
Operation	6	2.0	2.0	1.8
	7	2.8	2.8	2.6
	8	3.6	3.6	3.4
	9	4.5	4.5	4.3
	10	5.4	5.4	5.2
	11–55 (p.a.)	5.8	5.8	5.6
Termination	56	−20.0	−20.0	−20.0

Table 18. Assumed cash flows for the three options of the case study

Note: The figures for the operating life in years 6–55 have been obtained by deducting the assumed operating expenses (£0.8 million p.a.) from the gross revenues.

	Option 1 Total: £ million	Option 1 NPV: £ million	Option 2 Total: £ million	Option 2 NPV: £ million	Option 3 Total: £ million	Option 3 NPV: £ million
Total capital	−68.00	−57.19	−62.00	−51.90	−58.00	−48.69
Total operating expenses	−40.00	−9.42	−40.00	−9.42	−40.00	−9.42
Total gross receipts	+319.30	+70.68	+319.30	+70.68	+309.30	+68.33
Termination costs	−20.00	−0.77	−20.00	−0.77	−20.00	−0.77
		+3.30		+8.59		+9.45

Table 19. Summary of the cash flows for the three options of the case study.

	NPV Option 1: £ million	NPV Option 2: £ million	NPV Option 3: £ million
Slightly optimistic	15.59	20.62	21.07
Most likely	3.30	8.59	9.45
Slightly pessimistic	−8.99	−3.44	−2.17

Table 20. Results of sensitivity analysis

The weighted average NPV is £7.20 million. It will be seen that the NPV is negative, i.e. the project would make a loss, under scenarios 4, 7 and 10, although there is less than a 5% probability of this occurring.

There is a 0.5% probability that the bridge will be destroyed prematurely in its lifetime (for one of a variety of reasons). If this occurs in, say, 27 years' time, the NPV of the loss of net revenue is about £15.6 million, which would cause nearly all the scenarios in Table 22 to show a loss.

The following package of mitigation measures has been proposed.
- Let a fixed-price construction contract for payments having a NPV of £50 million.

- Insure against the risk of destruction by paying a premium of £30 000 p.a. If destruction occurs, the policy will pay a sum equal to the discounted capital value of all future net revenue.
- Purchase the ferry company for £5.5 million; it is assumed to have positive cash flows over the next ten years which have a NPV of £5.0 million at 6%, so there is a 'loss' of £0.5 million of NPV.

The first measure above eliminates C_1 and C_2. The second eliminates the destruction risk. The third is assumed to replace the bridge revenues sub-scenarios by those shown in Table 23.

If this mitigation package is implemented, we

would have the four new main scenarios shown in Table 24.

The weighted average NPV is £10.88 million. This distribution of NPVs is better than that shown by Table 22, since the weighted average has increased and negative values have been eliminated. It is still a matter for judgement as to whether the project is now acceptable, however, since the possibility of errors of estimation must be taken into account, as well as any risks which have not been specifically evaluated.

	Sub-scenarios	Range: £ million	Mid-point: £ million	Probability	NPV: £ million
Capital costs	C_1	57–59	58	0.8	–48.69
	C_2	59–67	63	0.2	–52.89
Operating costs p.a.	O_1	0.7–0.9	0.8	0.7	–9.42
	O_2	0.9–1.5	1.2	0.3	–14.13
Revenues p.a*	R_1	5.0–6.2	5.6	0.1	59.79
	R_2	6.2–6.6	6.4	0.8	68.33
	R_3	6.6–7.8	7.2	0.1	76.87

Table 21. Results of scenario analysis (Option 3)

* The figures quoted are for years 11–55; the figures for years 6–10 are assumed to be adjusted *pro rata*. Note: Sub-scenarios C_1, O_1 and R_2 correspond to the 'most likely' NPVs. Sub-scenario C_2 relates to the risk that construction is delayed or becomes more expensive for a variety of reasons, including a rise in the price of labour and raw materials. Sub-scenario O_2 envisages that wage rates may rise and more operatives be required. Sub-scenario R_1 relates to the risk that tolls may have to be reduced if the ferry company reduces its tolls. Sub-scenario R_3 relates to the possibility that tolls will not be constrained to present levels, either because the ferry company raises its own tolls or because the bridge proves able to charge a premium rate.

Scenario	Sub-scenario	Probability	NPV: £ million
1	$C_1O_1R_1$	0.056	0.91
2	$C_1O_1R_2$	0.448	9.45
3	$C_1O_1R_3$	0.056	17.99
4	$C_1O_2R_1$	0.024	–3.80
5	$C_1O_2R_2$	0.192	4.74
6	$C_1O_2R_3$	0.024	13.28
7	$C_2O_1R_1$	0.014	–3.29
8	$C_2O_1R_2$	0.112	5.25
9	$C_2O_1R_3$	0.014	13.79
10	$C_2O_2R_1$	0.006	–8.00
11	$C_2O_2R_2$	0.048	0.54
12	$C_2O_2R_3$	0.006	9.08
		1.000	

Table 22. Sub-scenarios combined into twelve main scenarios

Sub-scenario	Range: £ million	Midpoint: £ million	Probability
R_4	6.2–7.0	6.6	0.8
R_5	7.0–9.0	8.0	0.2

Table 23. Revenues after eliminating ferry competition

Scenario	Sub-scenarios	Probability	NPV:*£ million
13	O_1R_4	0.56	9.30
14	O_1R_5	0.14	24.24
15	O_2R_4	0.24	4.59
16	O_2R_5	0.06	19.53
		1.00	

Table 24. Four new main scenarios

* including the cost of mitigation measures

Appendix 9: Description of the RAMP process

Overview of the RAMP process

Activity A – Process launch
A1   Organise and define RAMP strategy

A2   Establish baseline

Activity B – Risk review
B1   Plan and initiate risk review

B2   Identify risks

B3   Evaluate risks

B4   Mitigate risks

B5   Assess residual risks

B6   Plan responses to residual risks

B7   Communicate strategy and plans

Activity C – Risk management
C1   Implement strategy and plans

C2   Control risks

Activity D – Process close-down
D1   Assess investment outturn

D2   Review RAMP process

Activity A – Process launch
(see Chapter 3)

A1 Organise and define RAMP strategy
A1.1   Confirm the perspective from which the risk analysis and management is being carried out and the principal stakeholders interested in the outcome.

This version of the RAMP process assumes that risk is being considered from the viewpoint of the owner client (i.e. the party which makes and owns the investment). The process can be adapted to suit other interests.

A1.2   Appoint the 'risk process manager', who will plan, lead and co-ordinate the risk analysis and management process, and report on its results. Define the reporting line.

A1.3   Prepare a preliminary brief on the objectives, scope and timing of the investment, including an assessment of its value and importance to the sponsoring organisation, and its complexity.

A1.4   Define and agree the provisional overall strategy for risk reviews and management throughout the investment life-cycle, including each of the following
- purpose of RAMP
- level of risk analysis to be carried out
- scope of review
- timing of risk reviews
- budget for RAMP.

A1.5   Ensure that this strategy for RAMP is fully provided for in the investment/project master plan and communicated to all parties involved.

A1.6   Form a RAMP process team by identifying and assigning those who will act as 'risk analysts' to identify risks, help to evaluate them and devise suitable responses.

A1.7   Introduce a 'risk diary' and maintain it throughout the RAMP process.

A2 Establish baseline

A2.1   Establish the baseline by defining the context and basis for the risk analysis and management process. This involves determining the information outlined in Section 3.2.

A2.2   Set out the RAMP strategy and baseline information in the 'RAMP process plan'.

Activity B - Risk review

(see Chapters 4, 5 and 6)

The risk reviews will be performed at crucial stages or time intervals in the investment life-cycle. The process activity for the first full review is described below. Subsequent risk reviews will revise and update the analysis and resultant actions.

B1   Plan and initiate risk review

B1.1   Review and confirm (or appoint) the risk process manager and the 'risk review team' for this review (refer to step A1.6 above).

B1.2   Decide on the purpose, scope and level of the risk review.

B1.3   Plan the review by
- compiling an action plan
- defining resource requirements
- establishing a budget and timetable.

Set out the above information, together with the aims, scope and level of analysis from B1.2, and the staffing and organisation for the risk review, in the form of a 'risk review plan'.

B1.4   Brief the RAMP review team using the risk review plan.

B1.5   Inform all of the other parties likely to be involved about the review, its purpose and timetable, and the names and roles of the people undertaking the review.

B2   Identify risks

The aims in this phase of RAMP are to
- identify, as exhaustively as practicable, all significant types and sources of risk and uncertainty associated with each of the investment objectives and the key parameters relating to these objectives
- ascertain the causes of each risk
- assess how risks are related to other risks and how risks should be classified and grouped for evaluation.

This is clearly a crucial phase. If a risk is not identified it cannot be evaluated and managed. The process of searching for and responding to risks is iterative.

B2.1   First, each risk analyst attempts to list the risks associated with each objective, key parameter, major 'deliverable' or principal activity within that risk analyst's area of focus. Make sure that every relevant aspect of the investment is analysed by the team of risk analysts. The first attempt should be from first principles without the use of any checklist or other prompts, to avoid constraining the process of discovery. Resulting risks are listed in the 'risk register'.

B2.2   Then the risk analysts should repeat the exercise with the help of the 'risk matrix' and other prompt aids such as

- checklists of problems from previous similar investments and projects, other case studies, technical papers, safety reviews and environmental impact studies
- site visits

- review of baseline plans, other key documents and outline designs.

List the resulting risks in the risk register for subsequent review and analysis, with a tentative indication of the significance of each risk ('clearly significant', 'possibly significant' and 'probably insignificant') and inter-relationships between risks. 'Significant' is to be interpreted as implying a risk whose potential consequence or expected value is such that it could have a significant effect on one of the objectives, parameters or 'deliverables', even if it has only a small probability of occurrence. At this point, no risks should be eliminated or ignored, because even seemingly minor risks can combine to have a major impact.

B2.3   Bring together some or all of the risk analysts, and others who can make a valuable contribution, for a brainstorming session to review the risks previously identified and to flush out further risks. The brainstorming should be in two parts: the first starting with the risks identified by the risk analysts, but without other prompts; the second attempting to find additional risk exposures with the aid of a risk matrix and any other appropriate prompt lists. Encourage participants to mention even seemingly unlikely risks and scenarios. Extend and revise the risk register in the light of the results of the brainstorming.

B2.4   It may be appropriate to interview or commission experts in particular aspects of the investment to identify risks which might otherwise be overlooked or not understood. It might also be useful to search relevant literature describing case studies of similar investments to learn about the risks they encountered, and the mitigation measures and responses adopted. Again, any resulting risks are entered in the risk register.

B2.5   Classify and if appropriate group risks to assist in their evaluation. Consider each risk in the risk register in turn to determine and record

- possible cause or causes of the risk
- trigger events giving rise to risk occurring
- possible timing and potential frequency of occurrence
- range of possible consequences – both physical and financial
- asset component, factor or activity associated with the risk
- objective, 'deliverable' or parameter impacted
- other related risks
- form of relationship with other risks
- who currently owns the risk
- the initial responses to the risk
- whether there are any risks which should be eliminated because they duplicate or overlap with each other.

B2.6   The analysis and understanding of risk groupings and relationships is often aided by representing them in the form of precedence, influence, risk/response or other diagrams, appended to the risk register with suitable cross-references.

B2.7   Update the assumptions list established at stage A2.1. Consider whether further identification work is needed: if so, return to B2.1.

B3   Evaluate risks

B3.1   For each identified risk which is 'significant' or 'potentially significant', assess in the first instance qualitatively and approximately
- likelihood/frequency of the risk occurring per unit time or some other convenient unit – i.e. will it occur once in every week, month, year, 10 years, 100 years, etc? (The paragraph below describes some ways of expressing likelihood.)

- potential consequence (with respect to one or more of the parameters or related cash flows)
- most likely frequency of its occurrence during the lifetime of the investment
- likely timing of its impact.

Note: risk assessment tables (see Appendix 4) may be a useful aid to prioritisation of risks.

The likelihood (or probability) of a risk event, assessed in the first entry in the list above, may be expressed in several ways

- once and for all chance of occurrence
- average rate of occurrence over duration of investment
- variable rate of occurrence
- physical extent of occurrence (e.g. per kilometre of rail track)
- probability of each of a series of possible values or ranges of values over the life of the investment (i.e. a probability distribution).

It is important to start with a natural/convenient basis for estimation, and link this to a life-cycle estimate. If there is a range of possible values, it may be acceptable, provided the range is not too wide, to represent the range by its mid-point or average value. If a risk is related to one or more other risks – in the sense that they share common causes or for other reasons the occurrence of one affects the likelihood of another – the related risks should be evaluated together. If the risks are not related, i.e. are independent, they can be evaluated separately. Enter the resulting assessment of each risk or group of related risks in the risk register. Include the risk that the assumptions shown in the assumptions list may not come true.

B3.2   Review the significance of risks and reclassify them into significance categories as at stage B2.2.

B3.3   For risks which are 'probably insignificant', decide whether the risks can be ignored, covered within a general risk category or retained specifically in the analysis. Do not ignore risks unless you are absolutely confident they are trivial.

B3.4   Identify as two separate categories those risks which could have

- serious or catastrophic consequences or high expected values
- exceptionally favourable consequences.

All the risks in both categories are likely to need particular, individual attention when assessing the overall 'riskiness' of the investment.

B3.5   Decide which risks justify and are amenable to more detailed evaluation and quantification. Generally, these are the risks with the largest expected values or, if probabilities are low, with the most serious consequences. In choosing the risks for further analysis, ensure that the likely benefit accruing from refining the estimate is worth the effort and cost involved. However, this does not apply to risks with catastrophic consequences (even if the probability of occurrence is low) as these are nearly always worth further study.

B3.6   For each such risk, conduct a more detailed and quantified evaluation of likelihood, consequence, timing, expected value and dependencies, noting carefully any assumptions made.

B3.7   For each activity affecting each parameter of the investment, compile an estimate of the potential impact of unknown and unforeseen risks over the phases of the investment life-cycle, based on experience and the complexity and uncertainties associated with the activity and parameter. It may be appropriate to do this by identifying general categories of risks and making a contingency allowance for each based on previous experience in similar investments. Enter the results of the evaluation in the risk register.

B3.8   Assess the overall impact of risks on each parameter affecting the investment, using a scenario analysis (or computer-based Monte Carlo simulation if appropriate), and carefully note any assumptions made.

B3.9   Using the investment model and parameter estimates, determine the overall impact of risks on the whole-life NPV of the investment.

B3.10   Conduct a sensitivity analysis, exploring the range of NPV for potential variations in the parameter values associated with each of the principal risks (including those with possibly favourable outcomes). This addresses 'second-order' risks, associated with the parameter assumptions, to assess confidence in the quantification of expected values and volatility measures. Assumptions like 'independence' can be tested in this framework, but general 'robustness' tests are difficult, and it is important to be sensitive to the impact of key assumptions.

B3.11   Make a preliminary assessment of the major risks which can be avoided, transferred or reduced in other ways (see mitigation measures in B4 below) by
- deciding provisionally – for each significant risk in the risk register – whether it could and should be avoided, reduced or accepted.
- making a preliminary decision on the most appropriate form of action for risk avoidance, reduction or containment, stating multiple options where relevant, and recording in the risk register.

- assessing the likely effect of the mitigating actions on the risk and its expected impact, including cost of action and bearing in mind 'secondary risks' resulting from the actions, and recording in the risk register.

B3.12   Consider residual risks and decide whether it is worthwhile proceeding to detailed planning of risk mitigation measures (B4).

B4   Mitigate risks

B4.1   For each risk (other than those designated as negligible), decide what are the main options for avoiding, reducing, transferring or containing risks, by considering such actions as those listed below.

Reducing or eliminating risk: Risks can be reduced by re-designing, changing methods and/or materials, value engineering or changing contracting strategy.

Transferring risk: Risks can be re-assigned to the parties best able to control them or (if different) who will carry the risks at lowest cost – e.g. to government, contractors, concessionaires, operators, bankers, and other parties through contracts, financial agreements, franchise agreements, bonds and guarantees and other 'financial instruments'.

Insuring risk: Insurance is a particular form of third party risk transfer applicable to some categories of risk (see Appendix 5).

Avoiding risk: Risks can be avoided by changing the scope, design, and/or technology. In extreme cases, substituting for or abandoning the investment may be the only way a risk can be avoided.

Absorbing or pooling risk: Where two or more parties are each able to exercise partial control over the incidence and impact of risk, agreeing to share any adverse consequences can be an effective approach to mitigation.

Reducing uncertainty: Better information can be obtained on the probability distribution defining the risk and its potential impact, through feasibility studies or specific research.

The effect of the risk mitigation measures will generally be to reduce downside volatility of the NPV, avoid worse case scenarios or improve prospects for favourable opportunities (e.g. increased potential revenue), but at the likely cost of a reduced expected NPV (because of the cost of the mitigation measures). However, increasing risk efficiency by simultaneously reducing expected cost and volatility is often possible and should be sought.

B4.2　　Evaluate each option for mitigation, assessing

- likely effect on risk, consequence and expected value
- feasibility and cost of implementing the option
- any 'secondary risks' resulting from the option
- further mitigating actions to respond to secondary risks
- overall impact of each option on cash flows.

Record options considered in the risk register. For this purpose, risk/response diagrams can be particularly useful.

B4.3　　Choose the most effective option or options and record with reasons for the choice in risk register.

B4.4　　Devise an action plan to implement each option.

B4.5　　Group together common or related actions which mitigate several risks simultaneously.

B4.6　　Compile a 'risk mitigation strategy', comprising all of the selected actions and the associated implementation plans, and include a 'risk account' showing the costs and benefits of each mitigation measure.

B4.7　　Using the investment model, recalculate the NPV to take account of the effect of the selected mitigation measures.

B4.8　　Consider whether a better result can be obtained by excluding those mitigation actions which have a high cost but limited beneficial effect on volatility. Some risks may need to be absorbed, unmitigated or only partially mitigated, because complete mitigation would be impracticable or too costly.

B4.9　　Select risks which warrant an in-depth study of possibilities for mitigation. Generally these will fall into two groups

- those risks where there are apparently worthwhile mitigation options but where confirmation is needed of their feasibility or cost
- the residual risks which are significant contributors to the downside volatility of NPV but for which no satisfactory mitigation measures have yet been identified.

B4.10　　For each such risk, evaluate options for mitigation repeating steps B4.1 to B4.7 above. Record the results from B4.1 to B4.10 in the risk register.

B5　　Assess residual risks

Residual risks are those remaining after mitigation measures have been taken.

B5.1   Assess the residual risks allowing for the result of adopting the selected mitigation measures, bearing in mind secondary risks and the cost of each measure.

B5.2   Sort residual risks into order of significance for each investment parameter.

B5.3   Using judgement, supported by Monte Carlo or other techniques, aggregate these risks for each parameter. Record the residual risks in the risk register.

B5.4   For each major activity affecting each parameter in each stage of the investment life-cycle, compile an estimate of the potential impact of unforeseen and unmeasured risks, based on experience and the complexity and uncertainties associated with the activity and parameter. Unmeasured risks are those foreseen risks which have not been measured or have been measured with a low degree of confidence. Consolidate these into contingency allowances for unforeseen and unmeasured risks relating to each parameter.

B5.5   Using the investment model, determine the overall impact on the investment (e.g. in terms of whole-life NPV) for each investment parameter, performing sensitivity analyses on the assumptions and estimates, and taking account of the contingency allowances in B5.4 above.

B5.6   In view of the expected value of the NPV, its volatility, the reliability of its measurements and the potential consequences of the major risks, reconsider whether the investment is still worthwhile.

B5.7   Determine whether there is a version of the investment which would achieve (or nearly achieve) the same objectives with higher expected NPV and

perhaps less volatility. If so, evaluate this alternative. Record the results in the risk mitigation strategy.

B5.8   Obtain formal approval for proceeding with the project and for the risk mitigation strategy, from the client and any other key stakeholders concerned (e.g. investors or lenders).

B6   Plan responses to residual risks

A 'risk response plan' is needed to minimise and contain the impact of remaining risks which cannot economically or practically be avoided or transferred.

B6.1   For each residual risk or area of risk, assign responsibility for containing the risk to an appropriate 'risk custodian' and designate other parties responsible for specific actions within the risk mitigation strategy.

B6.2   In consultation with the risk custodians and other designated parties, devise
- containment plans to minimise the risks and their impacts
- contingency plans to deal with specific residual risks should they occur and for each define the 'trigger' events or circumstances in which the contingency plans will be implemented
- contingency budgets for the potential impact of the residual risks on each of the principal parameters of the investment.

B6.3   If it is envisaged that crises will be dealt with by a 'crisis committee', its members must be appointed in advance, with back-ups in case of non-availability, and full details of home telephone numbers, etc., communicated to all concerned.

B6.4   If the risk impacts or costs of containing and responding to risks are significantly higher than previously estimated, go back to B5.5.

B6.5   Assemble containment plans, contingency plans and contingency budgets into a risk response plan.

B6.6   Obtain approval of client and other key stakeholders for risk response plan.

B7   Communicate strategy and plans

B7.1   At the end of the risk review, the risk process manager will critically assess the effectiveness of the review and the manner in which it was conducted, drawing lessons from the problems experienced and suggesting improvements for future risk reviews. This will be achieved, partly by reviewing the risk diary and other documents produced and partly by discussion with the client's representative and each of the other main participants.

B7.2   Compile a formal 'risk review report' outlining the main results of the review – including the main risks and their likely effects, and the overall riskiness of the investment – and the main lessons from B7.1.

B7.3   The risk review report should be considered in detail by client representatives responsible for the investment, who will need to review the continuance of the project and decide when the next risk review will take place and how it should be conducted.

B7.4   Prepare to communicate the relevant parts of the risk analyses, risk mitigation strategy and risk response plans to those responsible for each remaining area of risk as described in steps B7.5 to B7.7. If the investment is to be aborted, go straight to Activity D (process close-down).

B7.5   Extract the relevant parts of the residual risk analysis, risk mitigation strategy and risk response plan relating to risks assigned to each risk custodian and other parties involved in executing the strategies and responses.

B7.6   Supply the risk custodians and other parties with the appropriate extracts. Verify that these have been received and understood, and that those concerned are committed to undertaking the required action.

B7.7   Encourage all those involved to comment on or make suggestions about the residual risk analysis, risk mitigation strategy or risk response plan, and give consideration to the implications of these. If necessary, make revisions to reflect the suggestions.

Activity C – Risk management
(see Chapter 7)

The results of the risk review – notably, the risk analysis, risk mitigation strategy and risk response plan – are then used to manage risks as part of the mainstream management of the investment. However, it is essential that the risk analysis, strategies and plans continue to be monitored and updated regularly as risk exposures change and risk events occur in between risk reviews. The organisation and processes for doing this must be embedded in the procedures for managing the investment as outlined below.

C1   Implement strategy and plans

C1.1   Ensure that, as far as possible, the risk mitigation strategy and the risk response plan are integrated with main stream investment, project and operating management processes, with single responsibilities and accountabilities assigned to named individuals for each action. In particular, ensure that there is effective follow-up to verify that appropriate plans and actions are implemented in a timely and satisfactory manner, e.g. contracts, financial agreements and insurance policies are concluded, 'trigger events' are observed, and payments made.

C1.2   Where special or exceptional actions are needed to deal with risks which cannot effectively be integrated within the mainstream management processes, ensure that clear responsibilities and accountabilities are assigned with reporting lines, or at least effective channels of communication, to the mainstream management.

C1.3   Ensure that any exceptional actions, required to contain or respond to risks outside the scope of main management activities, are co-ordinated with the main activities.

C1.4   Any significant changes or developments during the implementation of the risk mitigation strategy and the risk response plan should be reported to the risk process manager.

C2   Control risks

C2.1   Verify that the risk mitigation strategy and the risk response plan are adequately resourced and effectively implemented.

C2.2   Monitor progress against the risk mitigation strategy and the risk response plan. Also monitor regularly all risks in the remaining stages of the investment life-cycle – not only the risks occurring in the present stage. Any significant changes in present or future risks should be reported and assessed immediately.

C2.3   Monitor risks regularly by studying events, situations or changes (sometimes called 'trends') which could potentially affect risks during the normal management and progress of an investment. These trends can be exposed through
- site visits
- progress reviews
- design meetings
- correspondence
- negotiations with contractors
- ground surveys
- market research exercises
- tests
- reports on other, similar investments.

These trends must be systematically identified, analysed and monitored on a regular basis by scrutinising reports, letters, and notes on visits, meetings and telephone conversations. Ideally, these should be considered at regular progress meetings (say weekly) involving key members of the investment management team. The trends can be usefully classified into one of three categories
- *potential (category P):* to be assessed or observed more closely
- *expected (category E):* mitigation or response measures to be taken
- *committed (category C):* measures taken and then either treated as changes to the investment baseline plans, after evaluating and allowing for their impact, or provided for in the risk mitigation strategy or risk response plan.

At each subsequent progress review meeting, the trends will be considered and may be eliminated or moved into another category. Generally, newly identified trends start in category P and then move first into category E and then into category C.

C2.4   As progress is made through the investment life-cycle, revise the residual risk analysis, risk mitigation strategy and risk response plan, and release contingency budgets, as some risks materialise and other risk exposures change or disappear

C2.5   When problems or significant changes in scope occur, revise relevant parts of the risk analysis, risk mitigation strategy and/or risk response plan. If significant threats, changes or developments occur, consider initiating an unscheduled risk review.

C2.6   Submit regular reports on progress, problems and changes to the client's representative and other key stakeholders (notably the project manager and operations manager).

C2.7   Regularly review whether the investment is still worthwhile.

C2.8   Decide whether (and when) a further risk review is required.

Activity D – Process close-down
(see Chapter 8)

At the end of the investment life-cycle, or on prior termination of the project, a retrospective review will be made of the investment (in terms of its success and risk history) and of the contribution and effectiveness of the RAMP process itself as applied to the investment.

D1   Assess investment outturn
D1.1   The risk process manager, in conjunction with the client's representative, will first evaluate the performance of the investment, comparing its results with the original objectives.

D1.2   Using risk review reports and the risk diary, an assessment will be made of the risks and impacts which occurred in comparison with those anticipated, highlighting risks which were not foreseen or grossly miscalculated.

D2   Review RAMP process
D2.1   The risk process manager will then critically assess the effectiveness of the process and the manner in which it was conducted for this investment, drawing lessons from the problems experienced and suggesting improvements for future investments. This will be done, partly by reviewing the risk diary, RAMP review reports and other documents produced, and partly by discussion with the client and each of the other main participants.

D2.2   The results of the review will be recorded in a 'RAMP close-down report', which can be easily referred to for future investments.

D2.3   Copies of the report will be circulated to all parties involved and then signed off by every party as an agreed record of events.

Appendix 10: Flowcharts of the RAMP process

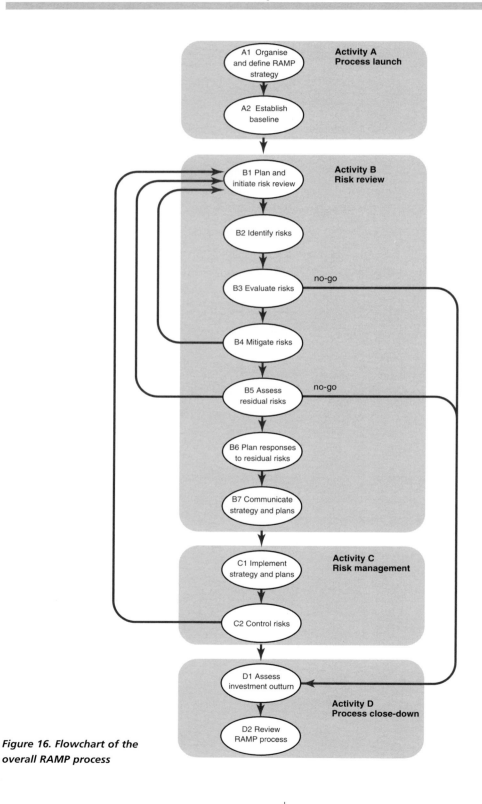

Figure 16. Flowchart of the overall RAMP process

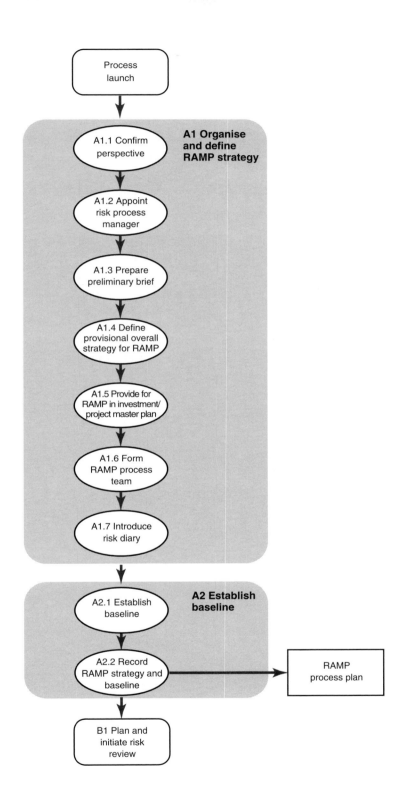

Figure 17. Activity A – Process launch

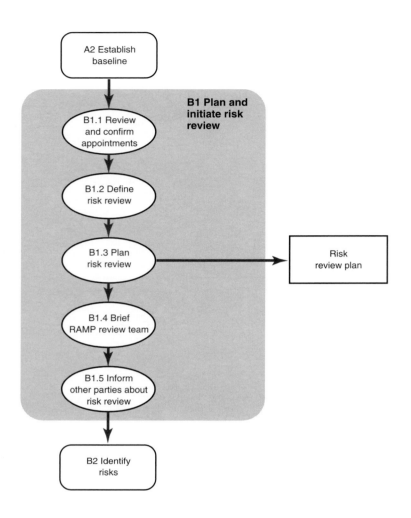

Figure 18. Activity B – Risk review: B1 plan and initiate risk review

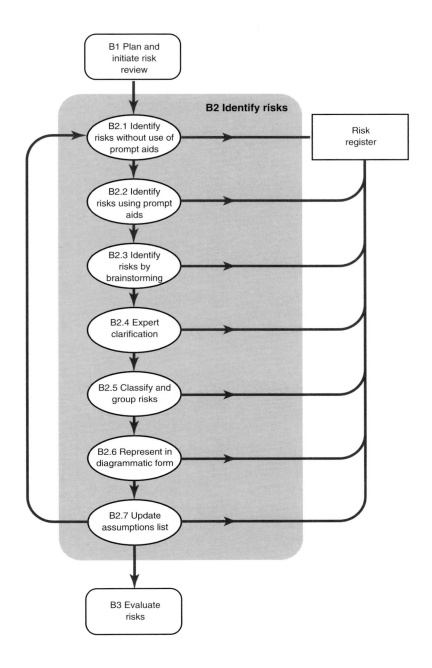

Figure 19. Activity B – Risk review: B2 identify risks

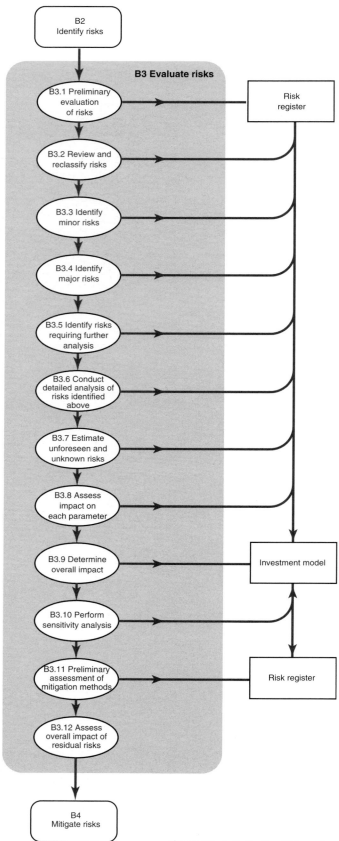

Figure 20. Activity B – Risk review: B3 evaluate risks

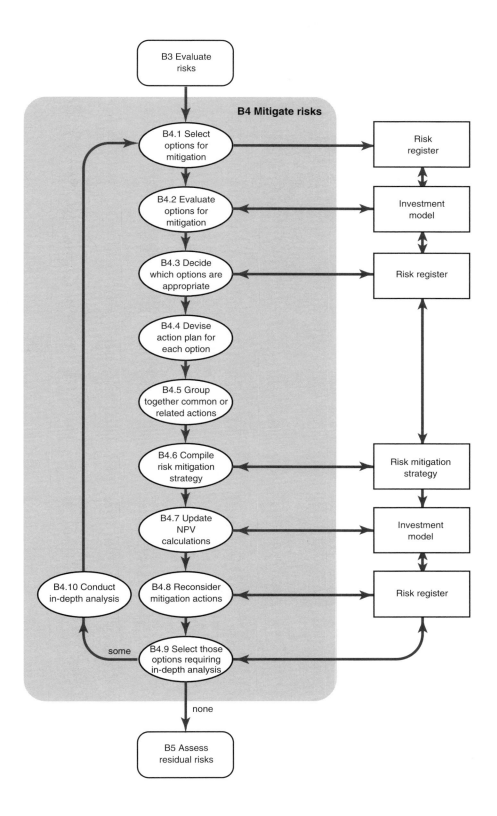

Figure 21. Activity B – Risk review: B4 mitigate risks

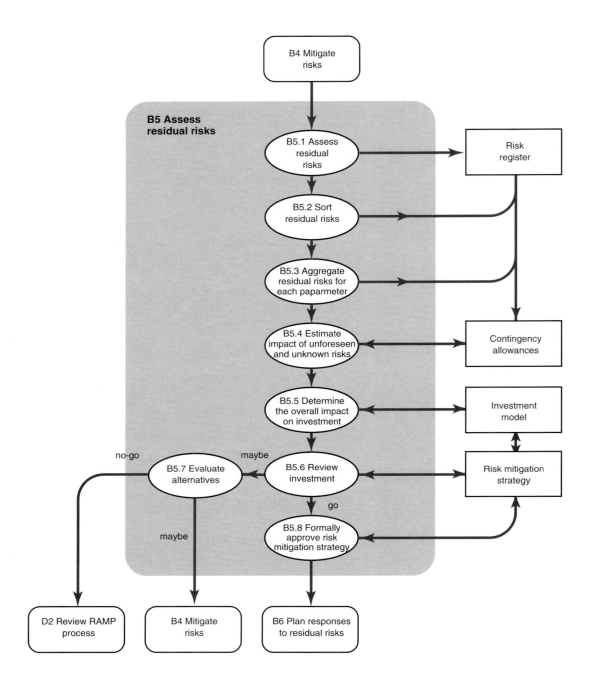

Figure 22. Activity B – Risk review: B5 assess residual risks

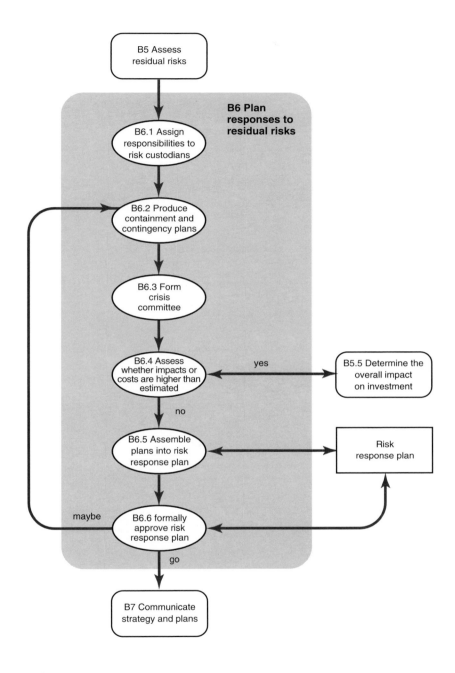

Figure 23. Activity B – Risk review: B6 plan responses to residual risks

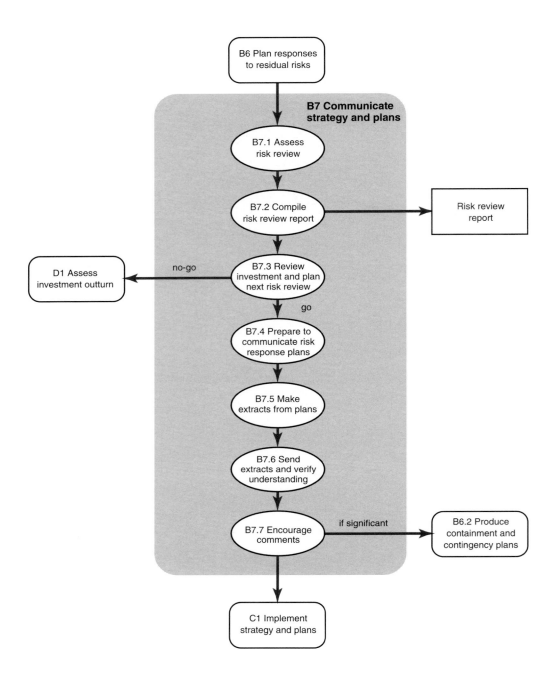

Figure 24. Activity B – Risk review: B7 communicate strategy and plans

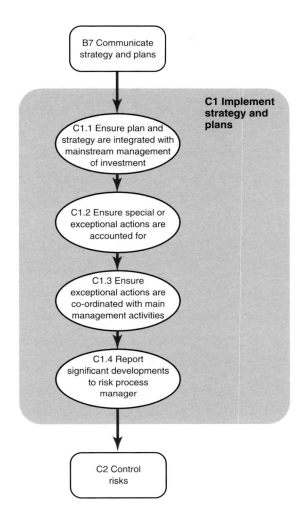

Figure 25. Activity C – Risk management: C1 implement strategy and plans

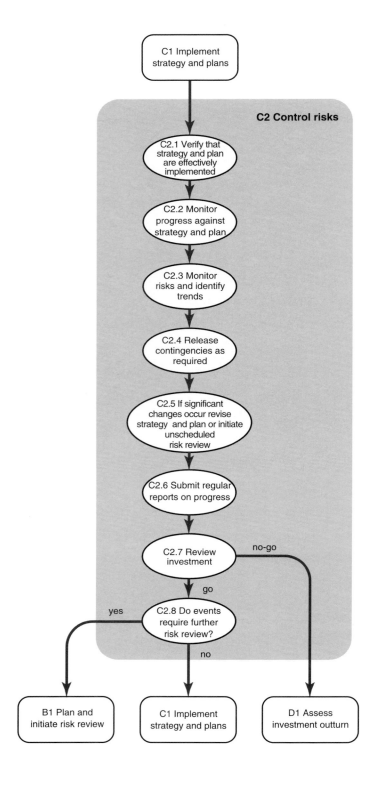

Figure 26. Activity C – Risk management: C2 control risks

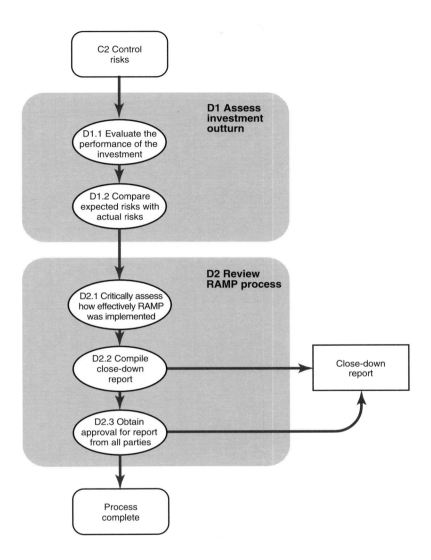

Figure 27. Activity D – Process close-down

Appendix 11: Key documents created in the RAMP process

Document	Purpose	Contents
RAMP process plan	To define strategy and basis for undertaking RAMP process over whole life of investment.	Investment brief and perspective, organisation and strategy for RAMP process, and baseline information.
Risk diary	To record significant events, issues and outcomes during RAMP process.	Significant events, problems, results, ideas for improvement and unforeseen risks arising.
Risk review plan	To describe the plan for carrying out a specific, individual risk review.	Risk process manager and review team. Purpose, scope and level of review. Action plan, resource requirements, budget and timetable.
Risk register	To record risk events and analyses.	Risk schedules: • Preliminary list of risks • Refined list of risks • Groups of risks • Mitigated risks • Residual risks. Individual risk analyses. Risk diagrams. Assumptions list
Risk mitigation strategy	To define the measures to be adopted to avoid, reduce or transfer risks.	Mitigated risks, mitigation measures, costs of mitigation and secondary risks.
Risk response plan	To define plans for containing or responding to residual risks.	Containment and contingency plans and associated budgets. Responsibilities for action.
Investment model runs	To record the data and results of each run of the investment model.	Timing and purpose of run. Scenarios modelled. Parameter values. Resulting NPVs.
Risk review report	To summarise and report on results of risk review.	Main risks and potential effects. Summary of plans. Riskiness of investment. Lessons learnt. Significant changes arising from review.
Trend schedules	To identify, evaluate and act on new risks or changes in risk exposures and outcomes during the ongoing management of the investment.	Events, situations and changes (trends) which could affect risks, categorised into • potential • expected • committed.
RAMP close-down report	To report on overall performance of investment and effectiveness of RAMP process.	Comparison of investment plan (as authorised) against outturn result. Summary of risk history. Assessment of RAMP process as applied to investment. Suggested improvements to RAMP process for future use.

Index

Practical Policing Skills
for Student Officers

Practical Policing Skills
for Student Officers

Editor
GARY WYNN

Contributors

DAVID CROW
AMANDA FORM
GARY FRASER
TREFOR GILES

LawMatters
PUBLISHING

Published by Law Matters Publishing
Law Matters Limited
33 Southernhay East
Exeter EX1 1NX
Tel: 01392 215577

British Library Cataloguing-in-Publication Data

A catalogue record for this book is available from the British Library.

ISBN 10: 84641 012 6
ISBN 13: 978 1 84641 012 3

Typeset by Pantek Arts Ltd, Maidstone, Kent

Printed by Ashford Colour Press Ltd, Gosport, Hampshire

Contents

Introduction

The role of the police constable in the modern police service is both challenging and rewarding. It is the allure of not knowing what a tour of duty may bring that attracts many people to the role. A tour of duty may require a constable to deal with incidents as varied as dealing with a lost child to being first on the scene at a serious incident such as a murder. When a constable leaves the police station or responds to a call on his or her personal radio, he or she does not know what the patrol may bring or what that radio message may contain.

Regardless of the incident, newly recruited police officers are provided with extensive training designed to equip them with the skills and knowledge to deal with a range of incidents.

This book accompanies and enhances those skills and knowledge. The chapters cover everyday incidents that a constable would expect to encounter:

- dealing with missing persons and the importance of taking the appropriate action when the report is received;

- aspects of the Theft Act in chapters covering the offences of theft (in the form of shoplifting) and burglary;

- the topical problem of youth disorder and the affects it can have on a local community;

- the everyday issue of dealing with drivers and their relevant driving documents;

- the emotive issue of domestic violence.

Each chapter provides you with an introduction to the scenario and puts it into the policing context. To reflect an actual incident, full details of the incident are then outlined to provide you with the information you need to progress through the scenario. Just as in an actual incident, the scenario can change and new dilemmas may be encountered that require you to make a decision. The chapters reflect this changing environment. Throughout the scenario you are asked pertinent questions in relation to the scenario and the actions you would consider taking. Each question is then answered.

The book seeks to link the practical aspects of these incidents to the relevant legislation, which is covered comprehensively. The chapters are also linked to the relevant units contained in the NVQ level 3 Policing award.

The team compiling this book have extensive police experience and knowledge in a variety of roles, which they bring to this exploration of everyday policing incidents

Chapter 1
Missing Persons

This chapter covers the following units of the National Occupational Standards for Policing (level 3):

1A4 Foster people's equality, diversity and rights.

2C1 Provide initial response to incidents.

2H1 Interview victims and witnesses.

Introduction – 'The golden hour'

During major investigations such as murder, the first hour is often referred to as the 'golden hour'. That first hour is the key to preserving evidence which if lost can impede an investigation. Research indicates that in child abductions resulting in murder, most of the children are killed within six hours of being taken. There is no time to lose. This must be borne in mind when conducting any missing person enquiry.

The scenario

You are on patrol; it is 16:00 hours on a Saturday when you receive a call to attend 3 Kingston Park, where Mr and Mrs May report their son Tim missing.

 What do you know?

What do you need to know?

How are you going to find that out?

What next?

What do you know?

Are you clear about the information received? If not, now is the time to clarify.

What do you need to know?

To be able to provide an effective service you will need answers to many questions. It is your job to find those answers, but first be clear about what information you require.

Useful information would include the following:

- How old is Tim?

- Does he have any medical conditions?

- Where is he missing from?

- When and where was he last seen?

- Who was the last person to see him?

- Who was he with?

- Which locations does he frequent?

- Did he leave any message/note?

- Has he ever gone missing before? If so, where did he go and when did he turn up?

- Has his other, usual behaviour changed?

- Does he have a mobile telephone with him?

- Does he use the internet?

How are you going to find that out?

Your starting point is Mr and Mrs May, who have reported the incident to the police. They will be worried and you will need to bear this in mind when dealing with them. Nevertheless, you are conducting an investigation and need to obtain accurate information in an impartial manner.

Mr and Mrs May provide you with the following information:

- Tim is 11 years old.
- He is fit, healthy and not receiving any medical treatment.
- He is missing from his home address.
- He was last seen at 11.00 am.
- Mrs May was the last person to see him.
- He was with his school friend, Martin Burke.
- He normally frequents Bullocksteads Sports and Youth Activity Centre to meet with friends.
- Tim told his mother that he would be back home at 2 pm as he was to go shopping with his parents.
- He did not leave any messages.
- His behaviour has not changed recently, he has never gone missing before and he appeared his normal self.
- He has a mobile telephone but there is no answer when it is called.
- He does not use the internet at home.

What next?

You have been given a lot of information and must assess each piece and its relevance to your enquiry.

Tim is 11 years old

Whilst children mature at different rates and each person must be treated as an individual, it is reasonable to assume that an 11-year-old child is vulnerable owing to his age and lack of life skills. You will also need to know whether he looks young or old for his age, as this may affect the way in which he appears to potential witnesses or offenders.

He is fit and healthy

It is very important to establish whether a missing person is suffering from any medical condition which, if untreated, would render him vulnerable and likely to come to harm. Consider a missing person with such a medical condition. What information do you require?

Useful information would include the following:

+ What is the condition?

+ What medication is required?

+ What are the consequences if not treated?

+ Does the missing person have medication with him? Check the quantity taken, as this can often indicate a person's intentions.

He is missing from the home address

One of the most important points to consider when investigating a report of a missing person is 'to clear the ground from under your feet' – a very basic but crucial course of action. It is not unusual for people to be reported missing when in fact they are still on the premises. Young children in particular have been known to hide in cupboards, under beds, even in lofts.

Be methodical with your searching, even if the person reporting assures you that they have checked everywhere. Sensitively explain that you need to check all of the property. Thoroughly search all rooms, large cupboards, under stair wells, beds, lofts. Check gardens, outbuildings and anywhere that could conceal a person.

As well as providing a physical check, conducting a thorough search affords you the opportunity to build a picture of the missing person's lifestyle, habits and interests. This gives you the opportunity to discuss with the person reporting issues which may provide information that is not initially obvious.

He was last seen at 11.00 am

Times are important in placing the missing person. We now know that it is 5 hours since Tim was seen, fit and well, by his mother, and two hours after the pre-arranged meeting time.

+ Is it unusual for Tim to be late?

+ Would he normally make contact to explain any delay?

The time lapse can be critical if the missing person requires medical attention or medication. If that is the case then **you must inform your supervisor immediately**.

Mrs May was the last person to see him

Sensitive questioning can provide useful information:

- How did Tim appear?

- Was anything, no matter how small, different in his manner or demeanour?

- What exactly was said?

- What was he wearing? Was he in school uniform?

He was with his school friend Martin Burke

What questions do you need to ask?

- What is known about Martin Burke?

- Home address?

- Telephone number (including mobile)?

- Places frequented?

- Associates?

Tim normally frequents Bullocksteads Sports Centre

Another source of information:

- When does Tim go there?

- Whom does he meet there? Obtain a comprehensive list of friends and associates – they may have vital information.

- Is he known to the staff there? Have they seen him?

- Is the Centre covered by CCTV cameras? If so, check recordings for any sightings of Tim.

- Are visitors required to sign in and out of the complex? If so, check records for timings.

He said he would be back home at 2 pm

How often is Tim late? Does he normally contact someone (if so, whom?) if his plans change?

No messages left

Would he normally leave a message? If so, where/how would it be left? With whom?

His behaviour appeared normal

Has anything in his life changed recently? It may be an incident/event regarded as insignificant by others but which has had an effect on Tim and which he chose not to discuss, or which he may not have had the opportunity to discuss with anyone.

Is there anyone Tim confides in? Whilst you do not wish anyone to breach Tim's confidence, you must stress that Tim's welfare is the main concern.

There is no answer from his mobile phone

+ Is this normal for Tim?

+ Would Tim know what to do, whom to contact if he needed help?

+ Consider asking your supervisor to contact the mobile phone service provider. All forces have a nominated person, a Single Point of Contact (SPOC) responsible for liaison. By registering the number of the missing person's phone, if the phone is used at any time then a time, date and location can be identified. This information would greatly assist in any search for Tim. This is a serious step in the investigation, as to instigate such actions involves interfering with a person's right to respect for his private and family life, his home and his correspondence under Article 8 of the European Convention on Human Rights. However, should the risk to the missing person be serious then any interference will be justified, necessary and proportionate. In addition, Article 2 of Convention (right to life) would afford protection.

Risk assessment

An initial risk assessment must be made regarding the degree of harm the missing person is likely to experience. This will determine the urgency of the case and enable you and others to prioritise the tasks to be carried out.

All missing person reports are potentially the first indication of a major crime. The vast majority concern missing people who return safely at some later stage; however, initially you must investigate if only to reassure everyone concerned that it is not something more serious.

The Association of Chief Police Officers' (ACPO) *Manual of Guidance* places risk in three categories:

- low risk;
- medium risk; and
- high risk.

Each of these categories is examined further below.

Low risk

Here there is no apparent threat of danger to either the subject (the person missing) or the public generally.

Once the person's details have been recorded on the Police National Computer (PNC) and the Police National Missing Persons Bureau has been informed, missing persons at this level of risk will not require any degree of proactive involvement by the police to trace them. However, the person reporting the missing person may still require support. In this respect, contact with the National Missing Persons helpline or other charities may prove of assistance.

Medium risk

Here the risk posed is likely to place the person in danger, or the missing person is considered to be a threat to himself/herself or others.

This level of risk requires some degree of proactivity by police and other agencies in relation to tracing the missing person and supporting the person making the report.

For example, if it was approaching the hours of darkness and Tim had no known places of refuge or means of support, money or food, and if he was wearing inadequate clothing, he would be likely to suffer as a result.

High risk

In these cases:

(a) the risk posed is immediate and there are substantial grounds for believing that the person is in danger through his or her own vulnerability or mental state; *or*

(b) the risk posed is immediate and there are substantial grounds for believing that the public is in danger due to the person's mental state.

A high-risk situation will require the immediate deployment of police resources and a member of your senior management team to be involved in press/media strategy and/or close contact with outside agencies.

For example, if Tim required life-saving medication and it was known that he did not have it with him, this would constitute a high-risk situation. Timings are critical and it is likely that you would be guided by your supervisor and senior management.

Making the initial risk assessment

The information that you obtain is critical in forming an accurate risk assessment for this report, and in ensuring that the investigation receives the correct level of attention.

Based on the information that you now have, complete an initial risk assessment, making notes to substantiate your decision.

When considering risk assessment, take into account the following:

Is there anything to suggest that the missing person is likely to cause self-harm or attempt suicide?

- Has he or she done this before?

- Does he or she have the means to carry out such harm?

- Has any communication the missing person has left (or the absence of it) given cause for concern?

- Was the person's mental and/or physical state vulnerable or unstable when he or she was last seen?

If the answers to any of these questions are 'Yes', then consider the following:

- Where does the person like to go (favourite places)?

- Is there anywhere of emotional significance for him or her, eg family grave?

- Are there any places in the locality favoured by people committing suicide, eg cliffs, bridges, railways?

Is the person believed to have been the victim of a crime?

This is very difficult to judge with any certainty. If you think that the person might have been a victim, consider conducting house-to-house enquiries for any information that would assist in your assessment. Remember the 'Golden Hour' and contact your supervisor immediately. The need for specialist search teams will be considered by your supervisor based upon the information that you have obtained.

Family liaison

Frequently the needs of those left behind are neglected. When a person goes missing this often creates considerable emotional stress on the remaining family, relatives and friends. Regular contact should be provided in all missing person cases. In more serious cases the appointment of a Family Liaison Officer (FLO) may be required. The FLO is a critical link between investigating officers and the family of the missing person.

Is the person vulnerable by reason of age or infirmity?

Many young people appear to be 'streetwise', but it is important to remember that legally they are children and that they do not have the same abilities to look after themselves as do adults. Elderly people often become confused and may not be able to cope when removed from their normal environment.

Is the person suffering from some physical disability or mental illness?

Many people suffering from mental illness may have a distorted view of reality that can result in irrational behaviour. Consider seeking professional medical guidance.

Has the person been subject to bullying?

Bullying is the cause of an increasing number of suicides, especially amongst children.

Searching

The search procedure will be dependent upon much of the information obtained so far. Together with your supervisor you need to assess this information and plan the search accordingly. If the search is complex, or will be covering a large area, it may be necessary to gain the assistance of a Police Licensed Search Adviser (POLSA). The POLSA has specialist skills relating to the conduct of searches.

Interviews

It is important to conduct interviews efficiently and effectively, as this is the means of obtaining information critical to the enquiry. The interview process should be continuous throughout the investigation, based upon information as it is received. All interviews need to be conducted sensitively using the '5WH' model of questioning, ie:

WHO … is involved?

WHAT …do you know/did you witness?

WHEN … did this occur?

WHERE … did this happen?

WHY… do you think that?

HOW … are you sure?

Initial interview

This sets the scene and parameters for the initial investigation. Remember the 'Golden Hour' and the fact that some murders are first reported as missing person cases.

If possible, interview others in addition to the person reporting. Friends and relations can often provide information not known to the person reporting.

Return interview

When a missing person returns, the person reporting the incident often experiences many emotions, including anger. You must assess the situation and be sensitive to this fact, as your handling of this situation can have a major bearing on the quality of your interview.

Remember, people go missing for a variety of reasons, sometimes as a result of abuse by a family member or carer. If the interview is conducted in the presence of the abuser, the missing person is unlikely to discuss the real reasons for his or her disappearance. In such cases you will need the assistance of an 'appropriate adult', eg an approved social worker. Further, it could compound matters by returning the person to the place of abuse. If you suspect abuse of a vulnerable person, seek the assistance of specially trained officers from your force's vulnerability unit to ensure that the best interests of the vulnerable person are safeguarded.

And finally ...

Based on the information you have been given, it is likely that Tim is considered to be 'medium risk', for the following reasons:

◆ He is 11 years old.

◆ He would not normally be late for pre-arranged appointments.

◆ He has not been missing previously.

◆ He is not responding to attempts to contact him via mobile phone.

◆ This is out of character for Tim.

Whilst at this stage the 'medium risk' categorisation may be appropriate, it is important to remember that risk assessment is an ongoing, dynamic activity. It must be continually reviewed as and when any new information comes to your attention.

You now have the basic information necessary for a competent investigation. It is important that all your actions are documented on the missing person report in a timely fashion. This information is not only important for the purposes of the current investigation, but it will be relied upon by others if Tim goes missing again.

Chapter 2
Burglary

This chapter covers the following units of the National Occupational Standards for Policing (level 3):

2C1 Provide initial response to incidents.

2C3 Arrest, detain and report individuals.

2K2 Present detained persons to custody.

Introduction

The offence of burglary is defined by the Theft Act 1968, s 9 (see **Appendix**). Although the legislation may appear complex on first reading, it can easily be interpreted.

Basically, s 9 states that a person commits the offence of burglary if he or she enters a building or part of a building, without the owner's or occupier's permission, with the intention to commit one of three acts, namely: theft, grievous bodily harm, or unlawful damage. The offence can also be committed if the person, having entered the building or part of a building, goes on to steal or inflict grievous bodily harm.

The scenario

It is 18:00 hours on a weekday evening and you are on patrol. You receive a call from the communications centre directing you to attend 4 The Grove, Kingston Park. The occupants have returned from work and have found that the property has been broken into.

What do you know?

What do you need to know?

How are you going to find that out?

What next?

What do you know?

At 18:00 hours today a call was received, requesting the police attend the scene of a break-in at 4 The Grove.

What do you need to know?

- Where is 4 The Grove?

- Have the occupants disturbed intruders?

How are you going to find that out?

- If you don't know the location yourself, ask the communications operator for directions over the radio.

- The communications operator will have spoken with the person reporting the incident, so ask the operator if the occupants have disturbed anyone. This is important, as the offender(s) may still be in the vicinity and prompt action could lead to an early arrest.

What next?

Acknowledge the call and make your way to the address.

At 18:20 hours you arrive at 4 The Grove. You inform the communications centre that you have arrived. You are met at the front of the property by the occupant, Mr Tait, who tells you, 'I left home at 7.30 am this morning and made sure that the house was locked. I came home from work and found that the patio door at the back of the house was open. My new TV system has been stolen.'

What do you know?

What do you need to know?

How are you going to find that out?

What next?

What do you know?

◆ Between 07:30 hours and 18:00 hours a TV system was taken from that address.

◆ That at 07:30 hours the house was locked and secure.

◆ That the patio door at the back of the house was open by 18:00 hours and that a new TV system is missing.

What do you need to know?

◆ Has an offence been committed?

◆ If so, what offence?

How are you going to find that out?

The information already in your possession indicates that the owner of the TV system believes that it has been stolen. It appears that a burglary has been committed. An essential element will be establishing whether or not anything has been stolen. You need to be certain of this information before classifying the incident as burglary. In order to do this you must find out if the essential elements of the offence of theft are present. A person commits theft when he or she dishonestly appropriates property belonging to another with the intention of permanently depriving the other of it (Theft Act 1968, s 1; see **Appendix**).

Mr Tait informs you that the TV system was his property and that no one had any authority to take it without his permission. You are now satisfied that a crime (theft) has been committed, but more information is required before it can be established that the further offence of burglary has been committed. The constituent parts of the offence were outlined at the start of this chapter. In this case the circumstances are as follows:

◆ 4 The Grove is a detached bungalow in a cul-de-sac consisting of 16 dwelling houses. It is clearly a building for the purposes of the Theft Act 1968.

◆ The house was locked and secure when Mr Tait left for work at 07:30 hours that day.

◆ He tells you that no one else has lawful access to his property.

◆ The rear patio door is open; there is damage to the lock. Someone has entered the house and removed the TV system without the permission of the owner.

You are now investigating a burglary.

What next?

Mr Tait is a victim of crime and you must deal sympathetically with him, taking into account any circumstances peculiar to him. (Is he vulnerable? Does he need any immediate assistance to help him deal with the incident?)

You need to conduct a professional, competent investigation into this offence.

 What do you know?

What do you need to know?

How are you going to find that out?

What next?

What do you know?

+ A burglary was committed at 4 The Grove between 07:30 hours and 18:00 hours today.

+ This is a detached bungalow in a cul-de-sac of 16 houses.

+ Entry was gained by damaging the lock on a patio door at the rear of the house.

+ A TV system was stolen from the property.

What do you need to know?

+ Who committed this offence?

+ Where is the TV system? Obtain as much detail as you can that could be used to identify the system (serial numbers, post-coding or unusual marks). Get the owner's manual or guarantee documents if available, as they will have a full description and perhaps a photograph of the system.

How are you going to find that out?

Your actions at this stage are critical to an effective investigation. You, as the first officer at the incident, are in control of a crime scene containing much valuable information and evidence which may lead to the identification of the offender and the recovery of property.

Think forensic! What factors do you need to consider?

The house

- Has anyone else been in the house recently (other than Mr Tait and the offender(s))?

- Has any other property been disturbed?

- Are there any marks inside that were not present before the burglary? Footprints in flowerbeds, damage to surrounding property, etc?

- The patio door lock – preserve this as best you can. A trained crime scene examiner may be able to obtain crucial evidence from it.

- Are there any tools or implements in the vicinity that could have been used to force entry to the property? If so, keep them safe for forensic examination. This may involve covering the scene to protect it from the elements.

- Is there anything left at the scene that was not there before the burglary?

The offender(s)

- Has anyone been seen in the property?

- Description of anyone involved?

- Are you aware of any current intelligence relating to burglaries that may assist in tracing the offender(s)? This could include particular types of modus operandi (methods of committing offences) used by specific criminals in your area.

What next?

It is important to preserve any scene until a forensic examination can take place. Victims of such crimes often wish to tidy the property and clear up any mess caused by the offender. You should explain that it is critical to an effective examination that such evidence is not lost. Check your local force policy on the deployment of crime scene investigators and inform control if you need their specialist services.

Conduct a thorough house-to-house search in the immediate vicinity to see if anyone noticed anything suspicious or out of the ordinary, before or after the event in question.

On examining the scene you find a large screwdriver on the paving next to the patio door. Mr Tait confirms that it does not belong to him. You also notice a footprint in the soil adjacent to the patio. If possible, leave everything in place until examined by a crime scene investigator. If that is not possible then carefully move the screwdriver to a secure storage space, having first made a note of its exact position. The footprint must be protected – a dustbin lid or plastic bag could be used to cover it. You must give clear advice to the householder regarding the safeguarding of the evidence so as not to contaminate it.

While conducting house-to-house enquiries, you speak to Mrs Andrew of 6 The Grove. She tells you that she saw a man drive a van into the cul-de-sac at 15:00 hours today. She states that she saw the man leave the van outside 4 The Grove and make his way to the rear of the property. She did not see him leave.

 What other information can this witness provide?

Remember ADVOKATE!

♦ **A**mount of time the suspect was under observation.

♦ **D**istance between the witness and the suspect.

♦ **V**isibility, ie what was the lighting like, what were the weather conditions?

♦ **O**bstructions to the witness's view of the suspect.

♦ **K**nown or seen before; does the witness know the suspect and, if so, how?

♦ **A**ny reason for remembering the suspect, ie if the witness has seen the suspect before?

♦ **T**ime lapse between the first and any subsequent identification to the police.

♦ **E**rrors between the first recorded description of the suspect and their actual appearance.

You obtain a detailed description of this man: 6 feet tall, white, slim build with short, dark brown coloured hair, aged approximately 25 years. He was wearing a red rugby-type jersey, blue denim jeans, and white training shoes with three black stripes on the side of each shoe.

What next?

Continue with house-to-house enquiries. There may be more witnesses to this incident.

Mr Black of 15 The Grove tells you that he saw a blue van parked near to 4 The Grove earlier that afternoon as he was watching the TV. He did not see anyone with the vehicle.

Again, remember ADVOKATE. Having questioned Mr Black, you now know that he saw a blue Transit-type van. He could remember a partial registration number – PJ51***.

What do you know?

What do you need to know?

How are you going to find that out?

What next?

What do you know?

- The description of the man.
- Some detailed information about the vehicle.

What do you need to know?

- The identity and whereabouts of the man.
- The identity, owner/registered keeper and location of the vehicle.

How are you going to find that out?

Submit your information to the intelligence unit. They have specialist knowledge and expertise in profiling individuals. Intelligence identifies three individuals matching the description provided by the witness. All three have previous convictions for committing dwelling house burglaries; one is known to use vehicles in the process. This individual is known to be Peter Corry, 24 years (b 11.05.1981), of 23 Beech Road, Kingston Park.

Searches can be made on the Police National Computer (PNC) using partial registration numbers. The records show that there are two blue Transit vans registered within the area with numbers beginning PJ51***, one of which is not currently registered to an owner. The other vehicle is registered to a parcel delivery company, which confirms that its vehicle was not being used in the area at the time of the burglary.

 What next?

Evaluation of your information suggests that Peter Corry may be linked to this offence. Do you have sufficient information to arrest him?

The Serious Organised Crime and Police Act 2005 introduced certain conditions that an officer must consider before arresting a person. This is referred to as the necessity test. In order to arrest for the offence, the officer must be satisfied that one of the necessity test elements applies. The conditions are as follows, and may be remembered by using the mnemonic COP PLAN ID:

C   Arrest is necessary to protect a child or vulnerable person from another.

O   Arrest is necessary to prevent an obstruction of the highway.

P   Arrest is necessary to prevent injury to that person or others.

P   The offence is one of public decency.

L   Arrest is necessary to prevent loss of or damage to property.

A   The person's address is not known to the officer, or the officer doubts that the address provided is correct.

N   The person's name is not known to the officer, or the officer doubts that the name provided is correct.

I   Arrest is necessary to investigate the offence. The investigation must be conducted promptly and effectively.

D   Arrest is necessary to prevent the disappearance of the person.

It is clear that burglary has been committed and you now have reasonable grounds to suspect that Peter Corry is guilty of this offence.

You arrest Peter Corry at his home address and you search his house using your powers under s 18 of the PACE 1984 (see **Appendix**). What should you be looking for?

- Clothing worn at the time of committing the offence and seen by the witness.
- Footwear worn at the time that could link him with the footprint left at the scene of the burglary.
- Stolen property, namely the TV system.
- Tools that could have been used to commit the offence.
- The vehicle.

Remember, when seizing property linked to a crime think forensic! Consult your scenes of crime officer for advice and guidance if in doubt about the forensic value of an item.

You recover the TV system from the home address of Peter Corry (again using your s 18 powers).

What next?

Having arrested Peter Corry, you should present him before the Custody Officer and explain the reasons for his arrest. You need to be able to give enough information to the Custody Officer for him to be able to authorise the person's detention, and also make him aware of any relevant information concerning the person's health and welfare.

The next stage is to prepare to interview the detainee using the PEACE interviewing model. The PEACE model is as follows:

Planning and preparation – This is the stage at which you should consider your interview plan, what you are going to ask, what evidence you will present to the interviewee, etc.

Engage and explain – This describes how to cope with the special problems of getting an interview going and establishing the 'ground rules'.

Account, clarification and challenge – This deals with the central issue of obtaining the interviewee's account, clarifying this and, where necessary, challenging it.

Closure – This describes the considerations before closing an interview.

Evaluation – The key questions to ask about what was achieved during the interview and how this fits into the whole investigation.

The planning and preparation stage

Having obtained the necessary statements and before interviewing the detainee, it is necessary to prepare an interview plan. This will give you confidence when conducting the interview and ensure that the essential factors are covered.

Peter Corry admits committing this offence and, after consulting with the Crown Prosecution Service, you charge him with burglary. What should you do now?

It is important to keep the victims of crime informed about the progress of the investigation. Mr Tait should be contacted and updated accordingly. It is good practice also to update the other witnesses who assisted with the investigation, as well as to take the opportunity to thank them and explain that their efforts have helped bring an offender to justice.

Chapter 3
Youth Disorder

Introduction

It is the Government's aim to create communities where residents feel able to go about their day-to-day business and to live their lives in safety. Sometimes these communities can be blighted by the activities of a minority. Invariably it is groups of youths gathering at certain points or in certain areas that cause fear among residents or people visiting the area. The disorder caused by these youths is referred to within the police service as youth disorder. Almost all forces view it either as a force priority or as a local priority to address, such is the impact it can have on communities.

The scenario

It is 20:30 hours on a Friday night. You are driving a marked police vehicle on mobile patrol with a colleague, PC Scott, when you receive a call from the communications centre requesting that you attend Wellfield Road, Castleshire, for a report of disorder by youths.

What do you know?

What do you need to know?

How are you going to find that out?

What next?

What do you know?

At 20:30 hours a call was received, alleging disorder by youths in Wellfield Road.

What do you need to know?

+ What is the priority of the incident? This is relevant, because if it is a high priority call you have to respond within a specified time. The communications centre will need to know when you get there in order to log your time of arrival.

+ Who was the call from?

+ Do we have a name and address for the caller?

+ Does the caller want to see the police?

+ Do we have any more information as to the nature of the disorder or the number of persons involved?

+ Do we have any descriptions of persons involved?

How are you going to find that out?

◆ Contact the communications centre for further information.

◆ If any names have been given by the caller, get the communications centre to use the computerised information system to check for any relevant details recorded against those names.

What next?

◆ Where is Wellfield Road?

◆ Are any other officers attending?

◆ Acknowledge the call and make your way to Wellfield Road.

The communications centre gives you further information, ie the name and address of the caller, a Mrs Grey of 20 Wellfield Road; she does not want the police to visit her home as she fears there may be reprisals against her for contacting the police.

The caller has further stated that the disorder is a regular occurrence; gangs of up to 20 youths regularly congregate outside the general dealer's shop.

You arrive in Wellfield Road and see a group of approximately 12 youths outside the general dealer's shop.

 What do you know?

What do you need to know?

How are you going to find that out?

What next?

What do you know?

You know you have a call about alleged disorder by youths.

What do you need to know?

◆ Is there any disorder, or are the youths just congregating in the street?

◆ Is it a genuine call?

How are you going to find that out?

◆ You cannot call at 20 Wellfield Road as the caller has asked the police not to attend.

◆ If you have not been seen, you could observe the behaviour of the youths.

◆ You could approach the youths and speak to them.

◆ You could go in to the general dealer's shop and speak to staff members.

What next?

◆ You decide to approach the youths and have a word with them. As you approach the youths you hear one of them swear and make noises like a pig; you are unable to ascertain which youth it was.

◆ You recognise 2 of the youths, having had dealings with them in the past for disorder and drunkenness.

What next?

On recognising 2 of the youths you radio the communications centre asking for Police National Computer (PNC) checks on any information or any warning signals for either of them. You remain out of hearing of the youths whilst waiting for the (PNC) check in case either of the youths is wanted on warrant or for any outstanding offences. You do not want them to be able to hear your radio when you receive the information from the communications centre. Your colleague, PC Scott, walks on to talk to the youths.

Warning signals are entered on the PNC by officers who have had dealings with certain individuals in the past. They are a form of information system about an individual. The warnings can flag up anything about an individual, from 'violent', 'assaults police' or 'carries weapons' to 'requires medication' or possibly 'self-harms'. They are a source of information for officers when dealing with individuals.

What next?

Be aware of the personal safety of both yourself and your colleague. There are 12 youths at the scene and you are aware that at least 2 of them have previous convictions.

The check comes back from the communications centre. Both youths are recorded on the police systems: neither has any offences outstanding, nor are they wanted by the police for any offences outstanding, nor are they reported as missing from home.

On receiving the information you join your colleague by the youths.

 What do you know?

What do you need to know?

How are you going to find that out?

What next?

What do you know?

- ◆ You know that there is a group of about 12 youths outside the general dealer's shop.
- ◆ By their general demeanour they could have been causing disorder.
- ◆ The behaviour of one of the youths was disorderly as you approached.

What do you need to know?

◆ What have they been doing?

◆ How long have they been there?

◆ Who are they?

◆ Where are they from?

◆ Where are they going, if in fact they are going anywhere?

How are you going to find that out?

You talk to the youths but are not getting anywhere; they are not being noisy or insulting, but they are not being cooperative and are not answering questions, stating that they have not done anything wrong and are just standing about talking.

What next?

You have had a complaint that you need to investigate. Although the youths are being quiet at the moment, you need to satisfy yourself that all will remain quiet. You decide to go into the shop and ask the staff if everything is all right.

You speak to the shop owner and staff. The owner is an Asian man called Gurmit Singh; he has one member of staff, who is a white woman called Wendy James who lives locally. Both Gurmit and Wendy state that the youths have been outside the shop for the past hour and, although they have been a bit rowdy, they state that it is no more than the usual.

Both appear to be uneasy about talking to you.

They are either unable or unwilling to give you any further information.

What next?

You still need to sort out the situation as you have not yet resolved the complaint.

You are not happy with the youths staying outside the shop as you believe that they were causing disorder before you arrived and that they will continue to cause disorder after you leave. If you do not do something, the initial caller, Mrs Grey, will be dissatisfied with the police action.

You decide to have another word with the youths.

As you go outside the shop, one of the youths you know to be called Jaffa says something to his friends and they start looking at you and laughing. Jaffa is one of the youths you have had previous dealings with, and you have arrested him previously for being drunk and disorderly.

One of the youths throws a coke can in the air and kicks it across the road. The rest of the group laugh and look across at you and your colleague. You approach the youth and ask him to go and pick up the can; he replies, 'I am not a f***ing bin man; if it bothers you, you pick it up.'

You ask the youth his name; he replies, 'Donald Duck.'

 What next?

What offences have been committed?

What is your next course of action?

What next?

You again ask the youth to pick up the can; again he refuses, stating that he pays your wages so if you are that bothered you can pick it up yourself.

You point out the offence of depositing litter and inform the youth that if he does not pick up the can and either keep it or deposit it in a bin, you will report him for summons.

(Reporting for summons is simply taking the person's details and the details of the offence for which you are reporting him, and submitting a file of evidence to put before the magistrates' court. The individual will be summonsed to attend court to answer the charges put to him by the court.)

Two of the other youths, one of them being Jaffa, start to swear, telling you to leave their mate alone. PC Scott warns Jaffa and his friend about their behaviour and informs them they will be arrested if they continue with their current course of action.

The situation appears to be getting out of hand.

What offences have been committed?

• The youth who has refused to pick up the litter has committed the offence of depositing litter in a public place contrary to the Environmental Protection Act 1990, s 87(1) (see **Appendix**).

• Jaffa and his friend have committed an offence under the Public Order Act 1986, s 5(1) (see **Appendix**).

What is your next course of action?

You contact the communications centre and ask it to send other officers to back you up, briefly explaining the situation.

The communications centre calls back immediately, stating that the task force van is nearby and is travelling to your location: estimated time of arrival (ETA) 3 minutes. You make sure that PC Scott is aware of the information and that he is safe. The task force consists of a number of officers (anywhere from 2 to 12) who are on call to assist with any incidents where more officers are needed, generally disorder calls.

You again speak to the youth who has deposited the litter, deciding to give him one last chance to pick it up; he again refuses and, egged on by his mates, is more abusive. You caution him and inform him that you will be reporting him for summons for depositing litter. When cautioned he does not reply.

You ask him for his name and address; he replies, 'I have told you it's Donald Duck and I live in Disneyland.'

You inform the youth that if he does not give you his name and address you will arrest him under s 25 of PACE 1984 and convey him to the nearest police station to ascertain his name and address for the service of a summons.

The youth now refuses to speak to you.

You arrest the youth under s 25(1) of PACE 1984 (see **Appendix**).

What next?

You place the youth in the rear of the police vehicle, and you and PC Scott stand by it. The youth Jaffa and his friend approach the police vehicle, shouting and swearing; you again warn them about their language and conduct, but they continue to swear at you and shout loudly. You inform them that you are arresting them under s 5 of the Public Order Act 1986. They become even more aggressive towards you.

At that point officers on the task force arrive; you explain the situation to the officers on the task force van, and you caution and arrest the 2 youths, who are then placed in the task force van for transportation to the police station.

You return to your police vehicle to transport the youth arrested under s 25 of PACE 1984; you again ask the youth for his details, but he still refuses to speak to you.

What next?

The group of youths is still standing near to the entrance of the general dealer's shop. The youths are quiet, just talking amongst themselves. You ask them for their details and they are very compliant, giving you their names and addresses. You give them advice about their behaviour, inform them you will be back in the area in the near future, and then return to the police vehicle to transport the arrested youth to the police station.

Because of the youth's demeanour you believe that he may present a danger to you. Under s 32 of PACE 1984 (see **Appendix**) and whilst not at a police station, you have a power to search the person who has been arrested if you have reasonable grounds for believing the arrested person may:

(a) present a danger to himself or others;

(b) have concealed on him anything which he might use to assist himself to escape from lawful custody;

(c) have concealed on him anything which might be evidence relating to an offence.

What next?

You search the youth but do not find anything that causes any problems.

You transport the youth to the police station.

What do you need to know?

- You need to be aware of the time you arrested the youth.

- The location of the arrest.

- The grounds for the arrest.

- The time of arrival at the police station.

The Custody Officer will need this information.

The Custody Officer will want to know if you have searched the person and may require a further search to be carried out.

What do you need to know?

You need to be able to give enough information to the Custody Officer for him to be able to make a decision about the arrested person and what future action to take.

What next?

You outline the circumstances of the arrest to the Custody Officer, who asks the youth for his name, age and address.

The youth immediately gives his details to the Custody Officer. They are:

Paul Jones

28 Greenwood Gardens

Castleshire

dob 030286.

The Custody Officer instructs you to check the computer for the youth's details to verify his name and address, as the youth has no means of identification on him.

You check the computer and find the following information:

Police National Computer (PNC) Person by the name of Paul Jones dob 030286 Resides at 28 Greenwood Gardens, Castleshire.

Jones is recorded as having previous convictions for theft, but he is not currently wanted or missing. He has no visible scars or tattoos.

Would that be enough to verify the person's details as correct?

You check the Force Computerised Information system and find that a 'Paul Jones 030286' is again recorded on the system. Fortunately there is also a picture of Paul Jones on the system, and you can verify that the picture and the arrested youth are one and the same.

What next?

You inform the Custody Officer of the verification of the details and the Custody Officer immediately tells you to report the youth for summons.

You remind Jones that he is under caution and inform him he will be reported for summons for depositing litter in a public place contrary to the Environmental Protection Act 1990, s 87(1).

Jones makes no reply when cautioned.

The Custody Officer completes the relevant paperwork (custody record) and Jones is released from police custody.

What next?

You will need to complete the paperwork for the litter offence, but prior to that you have to deal with the 2 youths you arrested under s 5 of the Public Order Act 1986. They have been transported to the police station by the officers who attended Wellfield Road to give you assistance.

You confer with the 2 officers who transported the youth Jaffa and his friend.

What details do you require?

You confirm the time the 2 youths were arrested and the time they actually arrived at the police station. You also check to see if they were searched under s 32 of PACE 1984 and whether they have given their names to the transporting officers. You also need the names and numbers of the officers who transported the youths. All this information will need to be given to the Custody Officer.

What next?

You book the youths in with the Custody Officer individually, giving all the details you have and the circumstances leading to their arrest. Both youths give their full names, addresses and dates of birth to the Custody Officer.

The youth you know as Jaffa gives his details as:

Paul Orange

Date of birth 040685

Home address: 14 Albion Road, Castleshire

The second youth gives his details as:

David Webber

Date of birth 190786

Home address: 27 Albion Road, Castleshire

What next?

The Custody Officer tells you to verify the youths' addresses.

You check the PNC and find that both names are recorded: neither is wanted or missing; neither has any marks, scars or tattoos.

Both youths are recorded on the force computerised information system, but neither has a photograph on the system.

Force policy may dictate that an officer does a physical check on the addresses given by arrested persons if they have no other means of identification on them. This is done to avoid arrested persons giving false details at the police station.

What next?

The Custody Officer authorises detention whilst the youths' details are verified. You contact the force communications centre and ask it to detail an officer to attend the youths' addresses to verify them. You are informed that due to the heavy workload it will be some time before a unit is available to attend to the detail.

You liaise with the Custody Officer who instructs you to attend the addresses and verify them yourself. You inform the communications centre that you will attend the addresses to verify the details of the arrested persons.

The Custody Officer also informs you that once the addresses are verified, you will charge the youths with an offence under s 5 of the Public Order Act 1986 and they will be bailed to appear at Castleshire magistrates' court.

You attend the given addresses of both the arrested youths and verify their details. You then return to the police station and report to the Custody Officer.

What next?

The Custody Officer has prepared the computerised charge sheet for the 2 youths.

You charge both the youths with an offence under s 5 of the Public Order Act 1986, and the youths are bailed to attend Castleshire magistrates' court.

The Custody Officer endorses the relevant paperwork (the custody record).

Both youths are then released from police custody.

What next?

You have paperwork to complete for the summons for litter and for the arrests for s 5. You will also update the relevant information systems for your force, either on the computer or on paper.

What next?

As previously discussed, you will have the paperwork to complete for the summons and the arrests, but what about the original call? Was it sorted out to your satisfaction, or – more importantly – was it sorted out to the satisfaction of the original caller?

What could you do?

When you have completed your paperwork, you could return to Wellfield Road and revisit the shop. You were not happy with the response of the owner and female staff member. Was there more disorder than they were willing to say? Were they intimidated at that time? If you called at the store at some other time, could you possibly get more information? There are possible offences which need to be investigated, for example offences contrary to the Protection from Harrassment Act 1997.

What about the original caller – Mrs Grey of 20 Wellfield Road? Although she did not want the police to visit her at the time, she contacted the police by telephone, so the communications centre will have her number. Call her to see if you can make an appointment to visit her, or enquire whether she is willing to attend the police station to see you. During her original call she said that such disorder was a regular occurrence, so there may be a need for a greater police presence and possibly the need to gather information for other offences.

What about the local beat officer or community officers? They may have knowledge about the problem, or would certainly want to be made aware if there is a regular problem of disorder.

Although this evening you have made 2 arrests and summonsed a youth for an offence, have you sorted out the problem you were sent to deal with, or will it continue or even get worse for the persons concerned?

There are more enquiries and work to carry out before this job is finished.

Chapter 4
Shoplifting

This chapter covers the following units of the National Occupational Standards for Policing (level 3):

1A1   Use police actions in a fair and justified way.

2C1   Provide initial response to incidents.

2C3   Arrest, detain and report individuals.

2H1   Interview victims and witnesses.

2K2   Present detained persons to custody.

Introduction

The offence of 'shoplifting' does not actually exist in legislation or statute. It is a term applied to a form of theft whereby a person steals property from a shop or store. The offence crosses social boundaries and costs the retail industry millions of pounds a year. It can be commited by all sorts of people, ranging from well-organised gangs who steal to order from others, to those from affluent backgrounds, to schoolchildren or elderly people. The offence cannot be assigned to one particular group.

The scenario

It is 14:30 hours on a weekday afternoon and you are on patrol. You receive a call from the communications centre directing you to attend Nixon's department store. The security staff have detained an adult male shoplifter and are requesting police attendance.

What do you know?

What do you need to know?

How are you going to find that out?

What next?

What do you know?

At 14:30 hours today a call was received requesting police attendance at Nixon's department store, where a male shoplifter has been detained by security staff.

What do you need to know?

- ◆ Where is Nixon's department store?
- ◆ Where has the shoplifter been detained within the store?

How are you going to find that out?

If you do not already know, ask the communications operator over the radio.

What next?

Acknowledge the call and make your way to the security office at the department store.

At 14:35 hours you arrive outside the security office at Nixon's department store. You inform the communications centre that you have arrived. You enter the security office where you see Maria Whatley, the store detective, in company with the suspect. You say to the suspect, 'Listen to what the store detective has to say.' The store detective then says, in the presence and hearing of the suspect: 'I saw this man in the men's wear department, where he removed a leather jacket from its hanger, put it on and then left the store, making no attempt to pay. Outside the store, I challenged him and asked him to accompany me back to the security office.' The leather jacket has a 'Nixon's' barcode label attached to it and is priced at £149.99.

What do you know?

What do you need to know?

How are you going to find that out?

What next?

What do you know?

The suspect was seen by the store detective to select a jacket from a display, put it on and then leave the store, making no attempt to pay for the jacket.

What do you need to know?

◆ Has an offence been committed?

◆ If so, what offence?

◆ What do I need to know and what are my powers?

How are you going to find that out?

The store detective alleges that the suspect has stolen the jacket, which is theft. You have already been told what the store detective has seen.

At this stage you need to be satisfied that you have reasonable suspicion that the offence of theft has been committed. As the store detective has informed you that she saw the suspect take the jacket from a display and leave the store making no attempt to pay, this would amount to reasonable suspicion that a theft has occurred.

Theft is an 'arrestable offence', which means that you have a power of arrest should you decide it is necessary.

What next?

The man gives his name as Jake Rowlands, aged 25, and an address at Flat 3, Kirsten Court, Castleton; he has no identification on him. The store contacted the police and wants to prosecute.

Is it necessary to use your power of arrest? What factors do you need to consider?

 What do you know?

What do you need to know?

How are you going to find that out?

What next?

What do you know?

♦ You have a name and address for the suspect.

♦ The store wishes the police to take action and prosecute.

What do you need to know?

♦ You need to confirm the suspect's details.

♦ You can arrest the suspect only if it is necessary in all the circumstances. You should therefore consider what alternatives you have.

Your options are:

(a) formally to caution the suspect for the offence;

(b) to report him for further action to be taken by way of summons; or

(c) to arrest for the offence of theft.

Given the value of the jacket, the option of a fixed penalty is not available.

How are you going to find that out?

- ◆ You can confirm the suspect's details by using the various computer systems available. For example, the Police National Computer (PNC), voters' register or other computer system used by your own force.

- ◆ In deciding how to deal with the suspect, you should take into account the seriousness of the offence and the wishes of the victim (the store).

What next?

Having taken account of all the above factors, you make the decision to arrest the suspect.

It is very important that the suspect clearly understands what you are doing and that he is informed of the caution. It is also important to note the suspect's reaction to what the store detective tells you in the presence and hearing of the suspect.

 Write out what you are going to say to the suspect, including the caution.

An example of what you might have written is:

> You have heard what the store detective has had to say. I am arresting you on suspicion of theft of the jacket. You do not have to say anything. But it may harm your defence if you do not mention when questioned something which you later rely on in Court. Anything you do say may be given in evidence.

The suspect makes no reply.

You also need to record the time and place that this occurred.

 What do you know?

What do you need to know?

How are you going to find that out?

What next?

What do you know?

You have now arrested the suspect on suspicion of theft of the jacket.

What do you need to know?

- Transport to the police station needs to be requested, along with an estimate of how long it will take to arrive.

- Does the suspect have any other stolen property, or items which could pose a potential danger to you or himself?

- What is the proper procedure in relation to the seizure of the stolen property, ie the jacket?

How are you going to find that out?

- Using your personal radio, contact the communications centre to request transport and an estimated time of arrival (ETA).

- The suspect is now in your care and custody. Under s 32 of PACE 1984 (see **Appendix**), whilst not at a police station you have a power to search the person who has been arrested, if you have reasonable grounds for believing that the arrested person may:

  (a) present a danger to himself or others;

  (b) have concealed on him anything which he might use to assist himself to escape from lawful custody;

  (c) have concealed on him anything which might be evidence relating to an offence.

- The jacket is evidence that an offence has been committed and is an exhibit. All exhibits need to be clearly labelled and given an identification number which relates to the person who is to produce the item as an exhibit. This person is the first witness who has had contact with the item. In this example, the store detective has taken possession of the item in the security office and will be the person to produce the item at a court hearing. The item is given the exhibit number, which will include the store detective's initials and a consecutive number. Some forces do this differently from others.

In this case the exhibit reference will be MEW/1; this represents the store detective's initials (Maria Elizabeth Whatley) and the number 1, indicating that it is the first item she dealt with in this case. A label will then be completed using this reference, which will be signed by each person who has had possession of the property. It is necessary for the item to be retained and kept available for any subsequent court hearing. If the items in question are perishable (eg, food products), they can be photographed and the photo produced as an exhibit. With items such as clothing, you may be able to seize the item, retain it and book it into the property store at your station, or the store detective may sign a property retention form, promising to retain the item until the conclusion of any court proceedings.

What next?

You have requested transport and been told that a unit will be with you in 10 minutes.

You are satisfied that the suspect has no weapons or other items concealed on him that present a danger to you, him or others.

You have retained the leather jacket. The suspect also has another store's carrier bag, containing 5 T-shirts for which there is no receipt. You take possession of these items. It may be necessary for you to arrest the suspect later in respect of these additional items.

 What do you know?

What do you need to know?

How are you going to find that out?

What next?

What do you know?

- The suspect is now in your custody and you are responsible for his safety and welfare in transferring him to the police station until he has been accepted by the Custody Officer.
- You have taken possession of the jacket and T-shirts as you believe them to be stolen property.

What do you need to know?

- After your transport has arrived and the arrested person has been conveyed to the police station, you need to make a note of the time of your arrival at the station as the Custody Officer will ask you for this information.
- You need to know if the arrested person has any warning signals, and conduct a names check on the Police National Computer (PNC).

How are you going to find that out?

Having obtained the arrested person's name, date and place of birth, you need to carry out the PNC checks at the first available opportunity.

What next?

You are now ready to take the arrested person through to the Custody Officer.

The Custody Officer has responsibility for making sure that there are grounds to authorise the detention of the arrested person. The Custody Officer will want to know if you have searched the person, and may require a further search to be carried out.

You need to be able to give enough information to the Custody Officer for him to be able to authorise the person's detention, and also make him aware of any relevant information concerning the person's health and welfare.

Having already decided that you had a power of arrest, that the arrest was necessary and that you had reasonable grounds to suspect the person of stealing the jacket, you need to tell the Custody Officer this.

What next?

Write out what you would say to the Custody Officer.

You need to give the Custody Officer the following information:

- the time and place of the arrest;
- the details of the offence that gave you your reasonable suspicion and grounds for the arrest (eg, what the store detective said);
- what property you have taken into your possession and its location; and
- your time of arrival at the police station with the arrested suspect.

The Custody Officer has to decide whether there are sufficient grounds and reasons to authorise the arrested person's detention at the police station. If detention is authorised, it is the Custody Officer's responsibility to ensure that the detainee is fit to be detained and interviewed. Detention will usually be authorised for the purposes of preserving and securing evidence, and to obtain evidence by way of questioning. This requires you to obtain and record the necessary evidence, eg your pocket note book, the store detective's statement and recording of property in the relevant register. You will be required to carry out these tasks immediately, as the detainee must be interviewed as soon as practicable.

Having had his detention authorised, Jake Rowlands is informed of his rights. These include the right to free independent legal advice, which on this occasion is declined. The detainee is then searched and found to be in possession of £5.95 cash and two keys on a ring.

You will now be required to complete a pocket notebook entry in accordance with your own force guidelines. An example of this could be as follows:

14:30	Call received to attend Nixon's department store. Adult male shoplifter.
14:35	Nixon's department store, Union Street.
	Where I attended the security office and saw Maria Whatley, the store detective, in company with a man who I believe to be Jake ROWLANDS. I said to ROWLANDS, 'Listen to what the store detective has to say.' Maria Whatley then said, in the presence and hearing of the suspect, 'I saw this man in the Men's wear Department, where he removed a leather jacket (indicating exhibit MEW 1) from its hanger, put it on and then left the store making no attempt to pay. Outside the store, I challenged him and asked him to accompany me back to the security office.' ROWLANDS shrugged.
14:40	I then said to ROWLANDS, 'You have heard what the store detective has had to say. I am arresting you on suspicion of theft of the jacket. You do not have to say anything. But it may harm your defence if you do not mention when questioned something which you later rely on in Court. Anything you do say may be given in evidence.'
	ROWLANDS made no reply.
	I then took possession of the brown leather jacket (Exhibit MEW/1). I also took possession of a Maggs' carrier bag containing five T-shirts (Exhibit PCS3112/1), each labelled at £19.99, for which there was no receipt.
	Transport requested. ROWLANDS conveyed to Castleton Police Station.
14:50	Castleton Police Station.
	Documentation procedure conducted for Jake ROWLANDS, 14.06.1980, Welford Custody Reference CC509/05.
15:05	Pocket book entry completed re arrest of Jake ROWLANDS in Report Writing Room.

What next?

At 15:30 hours Maria Whatley, the store detective, arrives at the station to give a witness statement. This is not your statement but you will be required to write it.

It is essential that you ensure the key points are covered. One very important area will be the identification of Rowlands and what Maria Whatley was able to see him doing. These matters are generally covered in the list of identification points in the case of *R v Turnbull*.

The mnemonic ADVOKATE covers these issues:

◆ **A**mount of time the suspect was under observation.

◆ **D**istance between the witness and the suspect.

◆ **V**isibility, ie what was the lighting like, what were the weather conditions?

◆ **O**bstructions to the witness's view of the suspect.

◆ **K**nown or seen before, ie does the witness know the suspect and, if so, how?

◆ **A**ny reason for remembering the suspect, ie if the witness has seen the suspect before?

◆ **T**ime lapse between the first and any subsequent identification to the police.

◆ **E**rrors between the first recorded description of the suspect and his actual appearance.

When obtaining the description of the suspect it is important to avoid leading questions which might imply the answer, such as 'How short was he?' or 'How young did he seem?'. Use open questions, such as 'What age was he?', and ask if the witness can estimate a range (eg between 5'10" and 6 feet) rather than giving a precise height.

When describing a person there are 10 points to remember to cover the description in full:

◆ colour;

◆ sex;

◆ age;

◆ height;

◆ build;

◆ hair (style and colour);

◆ complexion;

◆ distinguishing features, eg tattoos, scars, facial hair, spectacles, etc;

◆ clothing (from top to bottom);

◆ whether carrying anything.

An example of Maria Whatley's statement might read as follows:

RESTRICTED (when complete)

WITNESS STATEMENT
(CJ Act 1967, s 9; MC Act 1980, ss 5A(3) (a) and 5B; MC Rules 1981, r 70)

Statement of: Maria WHATLEY   [   ] URN:

Age if under 18:   Over 18   (if over 18 insert 'over 18')   Occupation: Store Detective

This statement (consisting of 2 page(s) each signed by me) is true to the best of my knowledge and belief and I make it knowing that, if it is tendered in evidence, I shall be liable to prosecution if I have wilfully stated anything in it, which I know to be false, or do not believe to be true.

Signature: *M Whatley*   Date:

Tick if witness evidence is visually recorded [ ] (supply witness details on rear)

At 14:15 hours on (day and full date) I was on duty in Nixon's Department Store, Union Street, Castleton on the ground floor in the men's wear department. At this time I noticed a man standing by the coats and jackets section. The man was a white male, aged in his mid to late twenties, about 5' 8" in height, with short, spiky, mousey hair and a pale complexion. He was clean shaven and had small steel-framed spectacles. He was wearing a plain black sweatshirt and faded denim jeans, with black trainers with red stripes. He was carrying a green and white 'Maggs' carrier bag. My attention was drawn to the man as he appeared to be looking about the department more than at the clothes he was standing by.

I was watching the man for about three minutes from a distance of about twenty feet as I was standing by the shirts and ties. The lighting in the store is very good and I had a clear and unobstructed view of the man whom I have no recollection of seeing before. I now believe this man to be Jake Rowlands.

I saw the man select a brown leather jacket which he removed from its hanger and tried on whilst still holding onto the carrier bag. He was looking about himself all the time and appeared nervous. I used my mobile phone to contact the security guard who was also on the ground floor.

The man placed the empty hanger back on the display rail and then began to walk towards the Union Street exit, passing two tills before leaving the store, having made no attempt to pay for the jacket.

Outside the store, I approached the man in company with the uniformed security guard and said, 'I am a store detective from Nixon's and I have just seen you take the leather jacket you are wearing from a display and leave the store without paying for it. I must ask you to accompany me back to the security office.' The man made no comment and accompanied us back to the security office where the police were contacted. In the security office, I requested the man to remove the jacket which he handed to me. The brown leather jacket was a 'Nixon's' brand and still had the price label for £149.99. I produce this item as exhibit MEW/1.

At 14:35 hours that day Constable 3112 arrived at the security office and said 'Listen to what the store detective has to say.' I then said, in the presence and hearing of the suspect, 'I saw this man in the Men's wear Department, when he removed a leather jacket (indicating exhibit MEW/1) from its hanger, put it on and then left the store making no attempt to pay. Outside the store, I challenged him and asked him to accompany me back to the security office.'

Rowlands shrugged his shoulders. Constable 3112 then said to Rowlands, 'You have heard what the store detective has had to say. I am arresting you on suspicion of theft of the jacket. You do not have to say anything. But it may harm your defence if you do not mention when questioned something which you later rely on in Court. Anything you do say may be given in evidence.' Rowlands made no reply.

Constable 3112 took possession of the brown leather jacket (exhibit MEW/1). This item is identical in every respect to those sold in my employer's store.

No person has any right or authority to take any of my employer's property. My employer agrees to abide by any decision the police may make regarding this incident.

Signature: *M Whatley*

Signature witnessed by: *(Your signature)*

(Complete example of contact details and inconvenient dates here)

Home address: *C/O NIXON'S DEPARTMENT STORE, UNION STREET, CASTLETON, EASTSHIRE*

Postcode: *CA6 4DR*

Home telephone No. *N/A*   Mobile/Pager No. *N/A*

E-mail address (if applicable and witness wishes to be contacted by e-mail):   *mwhatley@nixons.co.uk*

Contact point (if different from above): *N/A*

Address: *N/A*

Work telephone No. *0161 2750855*

~~Male~~ / Female (delete as applicable)   Date and place of birth: *30.4.60 COVENTRY*

Maiden name: *WALLACE*   Height: *5' 7 "*   Ethnicity Code: *WI*

State dates of witness non-availability: *13–28 August*

	Yes	No	N/A
I consent to police having access to my medical record(s) in relation to this matter:			✔
I consent to my medical record in relation to this matter being disclosed to the defence:			✔
The CPS will pass information about you to the Witness Service so that they can offer help and support, unless you ask them not to. Tick this box to decline their services:			✔

▶

Does the person making this statement have any special needs if required to attend court and give evidence? (eg language difficulties, visually impaired, restricted mobility, etc) If 'Yes', please enter details.	Yes ☐	No ✔
Does the person making this statement need additional support as a vulnerable or intimidated witness? If 'Yes', please enter details on Form MG2.	Yes ☐	No ✔
Does the person making this statement give their consent to it being disclosed for the purposes of civil proceedings (eg child care proceedings)? (No box should be ticked on all three questions in this box.)	Yes ☐	No ✔

It is important to know the reason for interviewing a suspect. PACE Code C gives a definition of an interview:

> An interview is the questioning of a person regarding his involvement or suspected involvement in a criminal offence or offences which by virtue of paragraph 10.1 of Code C is required to be carried out under caution.

Having obtained the statement of evidence from the store detective, the next stage is to prepare to interview the detainee using the PEACE interviewing model (see **Chapter 2**, Burglary).

The planning and preparation stage

Having obtained the necessary statements and before interviewing the detainee, it is necessary to prepare an interview plan. This will give you confidence when conducting the interview and ensure that the essential factors are covered.

There are a number of points that you need to consider and include in your interview plan:

* What is/are the offence(s) and the 'points to prove'?

* What defences might the suspect put forward?

* What facts are known?

* What information do you need to know?

What is/are the offence(s) and the 'points to prove'?
The offence in this example is theft. Section 1(1) of the Theft Act 1968 states:

> A person is guilty of theft if he dishonestly appropriates property belonging to another with the intention of permanently depriving the other of it.

The key points to prove are:

(a) the suspect acted dishonestly;

(b) the property was appropriated;

(c) the property belonged to another; and

(d) the suspect had the intention of permanently depriving the other of it.

What defences might the suspect put forward?
Having identified the offence and the points to prove, the next thing to consider is what defences the suspect might put forward. In this example, some potential defences could be:

- The suspect did not act dishonestly (eg, the suspect believed he had a right to the property).

- The suspect had no intention of permanently depriving the owner of the property.

- Alternatively, the suspect may claim that he is not the person the store detective saw.

What facts are known?
The known facts in this example can be obtained primarily from the witness statement given by Maria Whatley, the store detective. These include what the suspect did (*the actus reus*) and how the suspect committed the crime (*the modus operandi*).

- At 14:15 hours at Nixon's department store, in the ground-floor men's wear department, the store detective saw a man described as a white male, aged in his mid- to late twenties, about 5' 8" in height, with short, spiky, mousey hair and a pale complexion. He was clean shaven and had small steel-framed spectacles. He was wearing a plain black sweatshirt and faded denim jeans, with black trainers with red stripes. He was carrying a green and white Maggs carrier bag.

- The man was seen to select a brown leather jacket, which he removed from its hanger and tried on whilst still holding on to the carrier bag.

- The man placed the empty hanger back on the display rail and then began to walk towards the Union Street exit, passing two tills before leaving the store, having made no attempt to pay for the jacket. Security staff detained him.

- In the security office, he was asked to remove the jacket.

◆ The brown leather jacket is a Nixon's brand and has a price label for £149.99.

◆ No person has any right or authority to take any property of Nixon's department store.

What information do you need to know?
We have already shown that the points to prove will need to be covered during the interview. In particular, it is necessary to try to establish the suspect's intent or *mens rea*.

◆ What was in the suspect's mind at the time?

◆ Why did he commit the crime?

Pre-interview disclosure of evidence
If the detainee requested legal advice prior to the interview, it would be necessary for you to decide what information you are prepared to disclose prior to the interview. It may be that you decide to disclose all your information to the suspect's representative at that time. Although there is no requirement for you to do this, it is unlikely that the suspect's representative will advise the suspect to take part in the interview unless there has been some disclosure of at least the broad facts and allegation.

Opposite is a blank 'interview plan' form. From the information identified so far, you can now complete the form.

Arrangements for the interview
There are a number of basic factors which need to be considered and organised before the interview can take place. Some of these are as follows:

◆ Is the detainee fit to be interviewed? This is a decision that the Custody Officer has to make when he authorises the interview. Factors the Custody Officer will consider include whether the detainee needs an uninterrupted period of rest and whether he has been offered a meal or drink.

◆ Is an interview room available? Other points to consider include whether there are enough chairs, the layout, and familiarisation with the recording equipment.

◆ If the detainee has requested the presence of a legal representative, is he or she able to attend?

◆ Have you obtained the necessary witness statements?

◆ What do you need to take into the interview with you? This will include sufficient tapes and labels, copies of statements or your interview plan, and any exhibits.

INTERVIEWEE	CUSTODY RECORD No. or Interview No.	DATE
OFFENCE		

POINTS TO PROVE (eg dishonesty, intent, etc)	DEFENCES (including possible areas of defence)

PURPOSE (of Interview)

RELEVANT ISSUES	
FACTS ALREADY ESTABLISHED (eg offence occurred at a particular time, suspect was wearing particular clothing. Should include significant statement/silence and those facts which may give rise to a Special Warning.)	FACTS TO BE DETERMINED (eg where was interviewee at time of offence?)

RECORD OF INFORMATION DISCLOSED TO SOLICITOR/LEGAL REPRESENTATIVE

Engage and explain

This is the first part of the interview and there is a set procedure to follow to ensure that the Codes of Practice are complied with in respect of interviewing suspects. Additionally, by following the step-by-step instructions on the card in the interview room, you will be ensuring fairness to the interviewee, and this will help to reassure you and to build a rapport.

Having placed the tapes in the machine, you must introduce yourself, state the time, remind the interviewee that he is still under caution, and read out the caution. If the interviewee has not received legal advice, he must again be offered the opportunity to receive it.

It is important to create the right atmosphere. This will include how you address the interviewee, establishing whether he has any immediate needs or concerns, taking an interest in his individual circumstances and, where appropriate, showing empathy.

Account, clarification and challenge

Having covered the formal procedures, you are now ready to obtain the interviewee's account. In order to do this it is important to start by asking an open question. An example of this might be:

- 'Tell me everything from when you first came into town today.'
- 'What happened from when you left home this morning through to when you were arrested today?'
- 'What happened today leading to your arrest?'

Remember to listen carefully to everything the interviewee has to say and do not interrupt. Once you have obtained the interviewee's account, you can then ask questions to clarify points. If the account differs from the accounts in the witness statements, you can then challenge the interviewee by referring to these.

It is important to use your interview plan to ensure that you cover all the points to prove, and that you produce the exhibits when appropriate.

Closure

Before closing the interview, summarise what the interviewee has said and be prepared to answer any questions he might have. There are a number of formal aspects that are required for the closure of suspect interviews. These are:

(a) stating the time the interview finishes;

(b) handing a notice to the suspect concerning his right to a copy of the tape (Code E); and

(c) sealing the master tape in the presence of the suspect (Code E).

Evaluation

Having concluded the interview, it is now necessary to return the interviewee to the Custody Officer. The Custody Officer will need to be updated as to the progress of the investigation in order to decide on the appropriate course of action, ie whether the person should be released with or without being charged.

When reviewing all the evidence and what the interviewee has said in relation to the evidence and points to prove, it may be necessary to revisit witnesses either to obtain additional evidence, or to clarify issues.

The final decision as to whether the person is charged, cautioned or released without charge will rest with the Custody Officer (assisted, where relevant, by the Crown Prosecution Service adviser).

Chapter 5
Driving Documents

This chapter covers the following units of the National Occupational Standards for Policing (level 3):

1A1   Use police actions in a fair and justified way.

1A4   Foster people's equality, diversity and rights.

2C1   Provide initial responses to incidents.

4G2   Ensure your own actions reduce risks to health and safety.

Introduction

As we work through this chapter, it may assist you to have your own driving documents to hand, as we examine each individually.

Road traffic legislation can sometimes be complex. However, the legislation relating to driving documents is straightforward and easy to understand. Regardless of the type of vehicle a person is driving, he or she must hold a driving licence for that class of vehicle, and the vehicle must be covered by insurance and, in some cases, by a current MOT test certificate. This chapter focuses on an everyday type of occurrence of the sort you are likely to encounter. Although you may consider the occurrence to be mundane or 'run of the mill', the underlying principles are the same for all drivers and vehicles you may have to deal with during your tour of duty.

The scenario

It is 08:25 hours on a weekday morning and you have been directed to patrol outside the Castleton Infants' School, School Lane, following complaints from local residents about parking in the area between 08:30 and 09:00 hours.

What do you know?

What do you need to know?

How are you going to find that out?

What next?

What do you know?

Local residents are complaining about parking in the School Lane area between 08:30 and 09:00 hours.

What do you need to know?

◆ Where are School Lane and Castleton Infants' School?

◆ Is there a contact to whom you can speak about the complaint?

How are you going to find that out?

If you don't know, ask the communications operator over the radio.

What next?

Acknowledge the call and make your way to School Lane and Castleton Infants' School.

At 08:30 hours you arrive in School Lane outside Castleton Infants' School. The school is located in a residential area and you notice that a vehicle has pulled up in front of the driveway of 32 School Lane, obstructing access.

What do you know?

What do you need to know?

How are you going to find that out?

What next?

What do you know?

The vehicle has stopped in front of the driveway of 32 School Lane, obstructing the residents' access.

What do you need to know?

- Is the vehicle on a 'road'? (A road is defined by s 192(1) of the Road Traffic Act 1988 as 'any highway and any other road to which the public has access, and includes bridges over which a road passes' (see **Appendix**). If School Lane falls within the scope of this definition, it is a road.)

- Apart from causing an unnecessary obstruction, are any other offences being committed or dangers being caused? (At this point there would appear to be no other offences committed. However, in similar circumstances it may be worth considering the offence of leaving a vehicle in a dangerous position as outlined in s 22 of the Road Traffic Act 1988.)

- If other offences are being committed, what offences? What do I need to know and what are my powers? (These will be covered as the scenario unfolds.)

- Who is the driver of the vehicle and who is the owner/registered keeper? (These are often different, particularly where the vehicle is a commercial vehicle or company car.)

How are you going to find that out?

With regard to the last enquiry listed above, you need to identify the driver and speak to him or her in order to establish who drove and parked the vehicle.

Remember, although establishing *ownership* of the vehicle will generally amount to preliminary fact-finding, trying to find out who parked the vehicle will amount to obtaining evidence about the person's possible involvement in an offence, and therefore requires the caution to be given if the answers are to be admissible later.

What next?

In respect of a person using a motor vehicle on a road, you have powers to demand and inspect certain driving documents. These include the driver's licence, certificate of insurance, and vehicle test certificate or MOT certificate. (For the definition of 'motor vehicle', see s 185(1) of the Road Traffic Act 1988 in the **Appendix**.)

You approach the vehicle – a blue Ford Focus, index TB01 HRP – and see that it is unattended. After a couple of minutes, a man walks towards you from the direction of the school and unlocks the driver's door.

 What do you know?

What do you need to know?

How are you going to find that out?

What next?

What do you know?

You know that the vehicle has been parked across a driveway and left unattended.

What do you need to know?

You need to identify the owner and driver of the vehicle, and establish if it is being used lawfully.

How are you going to find that out?

You need to speak to the man, explain why you are speaking to him, and ask him if he is the owner of the vehicle and if he parked it across the driveway.

What next?

At this point it is important to consider your personal safety when dealing with motorists. Try to avoid speaking to motorists whilst standing in the road. It is far safer to speak to the driver out of the vehicle, standing on the pavement or kerbside. If you are in a vehicle yourself, you could ask the person to sit in the back when you speak to him or her.

You speak to the man at the side of the vehicle on the pavement. You explain that complaints have been received about parking when children are being dropped off at the school. When you ask for his details he gives his name as Kevin Mark O'Reilly; he states that he is the registered keeper of the vehicle and admits to having driven the vehicle and parked it across the driveway. You ask to see his driving documents.

He hands you a driving licence; you now need to examine it.

What do you know?

What do you need to know?

How are you going to find that out?

What do you know?

- ◆ The man admits to having driven and parked the vehicle on the road.
- ◆ He has handed to you a driving licence for you to examine.

What do you need to know?

- Is the driver the named person on the licence?

- What is his driver number?

- Is the licence full or provisional?

- What classes of vehicle is the holder authorised to drive?

- Are there any conditions or restrictions on it (eg, does he have poor eyesight)?

- What is the date of issue of the licence?

- What is the date of expiry of the licence?

How are you going to find that out?

By examining the licence thoroughly you will be able to find out the answers to the above questions. In addition, you should bear in mind that a driver may still have a copy of a driver's licence even though he has been disqualified from driving. You can find out whether a driver is disqualified by carrying out a Police National Computer (PNC) check.

So far as the licence itself is concerned, although the format has changed over recent years, all licences contain the same information. With the latest driving licence it is important to remember that it is necessary to check both the paper counterpart driving licence, D740, and the plastic photocard licence.

The first point to check is that the name on both parts is the same. On the paper counterpart this is shown on the first line of the address; on the photocard the surname (or family name) is at '1.' and the driver's first names appear at '2.'.

The driver number should be checked next. This is located on the paper counterpart in the top right-hand quarter and at '5.' on the photocard. The driver licence handed to you has the following driver number: OREIL 706132 KM9FS. The driver number is a unique number based on the person's name and date of birth. Here the driver's surname is O'Reilly, and the first five characters of the number – OREIL – relate to the first five letters of the surname. If the driver's surname comprises fewer than 5 letters – such as FOY – the two remaining spaces are filled with the number 9, so that this section of the number would then read 'FOY99'.

The middle section of the driver's number – 706132 – is formulated from the holder's date of birth. The first and last digits – the 7 and 2 – relate to the year of birth, so in this case the driver was born in 1972. The second and third digits

– the 0 and 6 – refer to the month of birth, '06' referring to June. The fourth and fifth digits – the 1 and 3 – refer to the day of the month, ie 13th. You can now see that the driver's date of birth is 13 June 1972. This can be confirmed by checking the photocard at '3.', which shows the holder's date and place of birth.

If the driver is a woman, the number 5 is added to the second digit. Therefore, the second digit will either be a 5 or a 6 for a woman, or 0 or a 1 for a man.

The first two letters of the last five characters – KM9FS – refer to the driver's initials. The K and M here refer to Kevin Mark. If the holder has only a single initial, the figure 9 replaces a letter. The remaining three characters are for DVLA administrative purposes only.

The next matter to establish is whether the driver holds a full or provisional licence. This can be established by examining the photocard licence.

The categories of vehicles the holder is entitled to drive as a full licence holder are listed at '9.' on the front of the card licence. These are displayed again on the reverse of the photocard, along with the dates full entitlement was attained and the expiry date.

In this case the driver has a full licence for Category B, which entitles him to drive a motor car. As a full licence holder for a motor car, depending on the driver's age, this will also include authorisation to drive certain other categories of vehicle, including towing a trailer and driving certain goods-carrying vehicles.

Provisional entitlements are shown on the paper counterpart driving licence. If the licence is provisional for Category B motor cars, there are a number of conditions with which the holder must comply in order to drive the vehicle in accordance with the licence. These include:

(a) displaying 'L' plates on the front and rear of the vehicle, regardless of the class of vehicle. In Wales, provisional licence holders may display 'D' plates instead;

(b) being supervised by a person of at least 21 years of age, who has held a full licence for that class of vehicle for a minimum of three years.

The paper counterpart licence also contains details of the driver's history, including endorsements, penalty points, dates and types of offences.

On the photocard licence, the valid dates of the driving licence are shown at '4a.' and '4b.'.

If you are in any doubt whether the licence has been issued to the driver, there are a number of checks that can be made. These include checking:

- the photograph on the card licence;
- the driver number;
- the name and address of the holder;
- the date of birth of the holder;
- the issue and expiry dates;
- classes of vehicle the driver is authorised to drive;
- the signature of the licence holder; and
- the DVLA watermark on paper documents.

Having examined the driving licence, you now ask to see the driver's certificate of insurance. Mr O'Reilly hands a document to you.

 What do you know?

What do you need to know?

How are you going to find that out?

What do you know?

The driver has told you that he is the owner of the Ford Focus, index TB01 HRP, and has also stated that he drove the car and parked it in School Lane, Castleton. Under the terms used in the Road Traffic Acts, this could be phrased as 'driving a motor vehicle on a road'.

What do you need to know?

You know that in order to comply with the Road Traffic Act 1988, Kevin O'Reilly must have a valid certificate of insurance or cover note in respect of his use on a road of the Ford Focus, index TB01 HRP. Therefore, you are going to have to examine the document to check the following details:

- to whom it was issued;

- to which vehicle it relates;

- when it was issued;

- when it expires;

- what limitations as to use are imposed (if any);

- who issued it; and

- the policy number.

How are you going to find that out?

You now need to examine the document handed to you and check the details closely.

When you examine the document, you identify the following:

- the certificate was issued to Kevin Mark O'Reilly;

- it was issued in relation to vehicle registration mark TB01 HRP;

- it was issued at 00.00 on 24 September 200*;

- it expires at 00.00 on 24 September 200*;

- limitations as to use cover social domestic and pleasure, and use for the business of the policyholder;

- it was issued by Gladstone Insurance Services; and

- the policy number is MOT88245777528.

You are satisfied that the certificate of insurance is valid and covers the driver's use of the vehicle. You hand the document back to him.

As the vehicle has a registration plate which indicates that it was first registered more than three years ago, there is a requirement for the driver to have a valid MOT test certificate for that vehicle. If the vehicle has a personalised plate, or if you are in any doubt as to the date of first registration, you can always carry out a vehicle check using the PNC, which will give you this information and enable you to clarify the registered keeper's details as well.

You now ask the driver if he has a MOT test certificate, and he hands you another document.

67

What do you know?

What do you need to know?

How are you going to find that out?

What do you know?

You know the that the vehicle is Ford Focus, index TB01 HRP, and therefore it was first registered in 2001 and requires a valid MOT test certificate for its lawful use on a road.

What do you need to know?

The MOT test certificate contains information relating to the vehicle, including:

+ the motor vehicle registration mark;

+ the vehicle identification or chassis number;

+ the Test Station number;

+ issue date;

+ expiry date;

+ colour of vehicle;

+ make of vehicle;

+ approximate year the vehicle was first used;

+ recorded mileage;

+ if a goods vehicle, the maximum designed gross weight;

+ type of fuel;

+ tester's signature and printed name;

- certificate serial number; and

- authentication stamp with embossed details of the Testing Station.

How are you going to find that out?

You now examine the certificate and note the following details:

- the motor vehicle registration mark is TB01 HRP;

- the vehicle identification or chassis number is HOL0000412V3107824;

- the Test Station number is 1BLE60;

- issue date, 5 August 200*;

- expiry date, 4 August 200*;

- the colour of vehicle as blue;

- the make of vehicle as Ford;

- the approximate year the vehicle was first used as 2001;

- the recorded mileage as 38454;

- if a goods vehicle, the maximum designed gross weight marked N/A;

- the type of fuel as petrol;

- tester's signature and printed name as 'P Morris';

- certificate serial number as JEO134840; and

- authentication stamp with embossed details: Castleton Motors, Castleton CL2 8JF, VTS No 1BLE60.

Now that you have examined all his driving documents, the driver apologises for parking across the driveway. You now need to decide what action to take. Your options are to report the driver for causing unnecessary obstruction, or to give words of advice. Having taken all the factors into consideration, you decide to advise the driver regarding parking in the area in future and thank him.

What next?

You now need to make an entry in your pocket notebook in accordance with your own force guidelines. An example of this could be as follows:

08:30   School Lane, Castleton. Patrol re parking complaints

08:30   Parked and unattended across driveway of 32 School Lane, Blue Ford
         Focus, index TB01 HRP.

08:33   Kevin Mark O'REILLY, date of birth 13.06.72, 21 First Avenue, Castleton
         CL2 4PY. Driving licence number OREIL706132KM9FS. Returned to ve-
         hicle, admitted to being owner of Ford Focus index TB01 HRP and parking
         across driveway. Driving Licence, Insurance and MOT certificates checked
         and in order. Advice given re parking.

It is 08:40 and you resume patrol in School Lane. You see a vehicle pull up in front of another driveway. A woman and child get out of the vehicle and go into the school playground. You walk over to the vehicle, a red Vauxhall Astra, index V710 NWF, which has parked across the driveway of 7 School Lane.

When the woman returns to the car, you ask her if she is the owner of the vehicle. She states that she is. You explain about the complaints regarding parking and tell her that she is causing an obstruction by parking across the driveway. You ask to see her driving documents; she replies that she doesn't have them with her, that she is in a hurry as she is running late, and that she doesn't want to be late for work.

 What are your options?

What are you going to do next?

What are your options?

Again the offence of unnecessary obstruction has been committed by the driver of the vehicle. Additionally, it is an offence for a driver to fail to produce his or her driving documents to a police officer on demand. Your options are to:

◆ issue a fixed penalty notice for causing an unnecessary obstruction;

◆ report the driver for both the offences;

- issue an HO/RT 1 form for the driver to produce her documents at a police station;

- give words of advice.

What are you going to do next?

As the woman is in a hurry and you gave words of advice to the previous driver, you decide to do the same here as regards the unnecessary obstruction. However, as the driver does not have her driving documents with her, you decide to issue an HO/RT 1 form.

 What information are you going to require to complete the HO/RT 1 form?

The information you are going to require will include the following:

- name and address of the driver;

- the driver's date of birth;

- the vehicle's details, including make and registration;

- location of incident and, if different, where form HO/RT 1 was issued;

- the time and date of the incident;

- the time and date the request was made for the documents to be produced;

- what documents are required to be produced;

- the name of the police station at which the driver elects to produce the documents;

- your details as the officer requesting production.

By asking questions of the driver in relation to the above information you are able to record the following details:

- the driver's name and address is Rabinda Misra, 37 Castle View, Castleton CL2 8SY;

- the driver's date of birth is 14 March 1970;

- the vehicle is a red Vauxhall Astra, index V710 NWF;

- location of incident and issue of the form HO/RT 1 is School Lane, Castleton;

- the time and date of the incident and request is 08:40 am day/month/year;

- the documents required to be produced are driving licence, insurance certificate and MOT test certificate;

- the documents are to be produced at Castleton Police Station; and

- your details as the officer requesting production.

An example of an HO/RT 1 form is set out opposite.

When making the request for documents to be produced, it is very important to make sure the driver understands what is expected. You may find it useful to use the following example of what to say:

> It is an offence to fail to produce your driving documents to a police officer on demand and you will be reported for that offence. However, if they are produced in order at a police station of your choice, within seven clear days, no further action will be taken.

The driver should then be cautioned as follows:

> You do not have to say anything. But it may harm your defence if you do not mention when questioned something which you later rely on in court. Anything you do say may be given in evidence.

Remember to make a note of any reply the person makes.

Having completed the HO/RT 1 form, you must then hand the original to the driver to take to their chosen police station when they produce their driving documents. Most HO/RT 1 pads have two self-carbonating copies: the first needs to be forwarded to your administration department; the other one should be retained for your reference. Check at your station to establish where you need to send the administration copy.

HO/RT 1 This form should be produced with your documents

Full Name (Driver/Supervisor/Other (specify) ....) | Date of Birth

Ethnic Appearance ☐ (see cover for code descriptions)

Address

Postcode

Signature (Request only)

| Location of incident | Time | | | | | Date | | | | | |

| Location of requirement | Time | | | | | Date | | | | | |

VEHICLE								Yes	No
Registration Number.							Manual		
Vehicle Description*							Motorway		
							'L' plates		
							Passengers		
							Driver-supervised		
If motorcycle, include cubic capacity; goods vehicle include gross and train weight if applicable; passenger vehicle include seats (not driver's)							Rider with passenger		
							Trailer		

Use of vehicle SDP ☐ Business ☐ Hire of reward ☐

Documents to be produced (see explanatory notes overleaf)

Check only   1 ☐ 2 ☐ 3 ☐ 4 ☐ 5 ☐ 6 ☐ 7 ☐ 8 ☐

Record details 1 ☐ 2 ☐ 3 ☐ 4 ☐ 5 ☐ 6 ☐ 7 ☐ 8 ☐

At:.. Police Station

Issued by: Name: .... Rank and No.: ....Div. ☐ ☐

Reply to:

Central Ticket Office

Tick reason:

Accident	A
V.D.R.S.	V
Non. End. F.P.	F
Offence	O
Other	C

Having issued the HO/RT1 to the driver, you now need to make an entry in your pocket notebook. An example of this might be as follows:

08:45   Parked and unattended over driveway of 7 School Lane, red Vauxhall Astra, index V710 NWF.

08:50   Spoke to Rabinda MISRA, date of birth 14.03.70, 37 Castle View, Castleton CL2 8SY, who stated she was owner and driver of Vauxhall Astra index V710 NWF. Advice given re parking. Form HO/RT1 (Exhibit PCS3112/1) issued for production of driving licence, insurance certificate and MOT certificate to Castleton Police Station. I said: 'It is an offence to fail to produce your driving documents to a police officer on demand and you will be reported for that offence. However, if they are produced in order at a police station of your choice, within seven clear days, no further action will be taken. You do not have to say anything. But it may harm your defence if you do not mention when questioned something which you later rely on in court. Anything you do say may be given in evidence.' She made no reply.

08:50   Above pocket notebook entry completed in School Lane, Castleton.

It is now 09:15 hours and you resume patrol. You are walking into the High Street when you notice a green Peugeot 205, index S456 JAD, being driven in the direction of Church Lane. It pulls over outside J's Newsagents. The driver is sitting in the vehicle with the windows down and the radio playing loud music, which appears to be causing annoyance to some shoppers.

What do you know?

What do you need to know?

How are you going to find that out?

What next?

What do you know?

The driver is sitting in the car, a green Peugeot 205, index S456 JAD, playing loud music which is apparently annoying shoppers.

What do you need to know?

- What offences, if any, are being committed?
- Is the driver both the owner and keeper of the vehicle, and does he have valid documentation?
- You also need to ascertain the driver's details.

How are you going to find that out?

You need to speak to the driver and ask relevant questions.

What next?

You approach the car and speak to the driver, the only occupant, through the passenger window. You ask him to step out onto the pavement. You state that the music is being played too loudly and appears to be upsetting passers-by. The driver turns the radio off. You ask him for his name and address, which he gives as Aaron Gavin Stringer, Flat 2, Peak Towers, Whatley Street, Castleton CL1 3KR. He gives you his date of birth as 20 April 1985.

You ask if he is the owner of the vehicle, and he says that he bought it two days ago for £200. He states that he has sent off the V5C Registration Certificate to DVLA and hands you the 'New Keeper Supplement' for the vehicle, with his details entered into the New Keeper's name and address section.

You then ask to see his driving licence, insurance certificate and MOT certificate. He hands you an MOT test certificate which you examine and, having checked all the key details, find to be in order. You then examine an insurance cover note issued to Aaron Stringer at 12 noon two days ago. It covers use of the Peugeot

205, index S456 JAD, for 30 days from the date of issue for social domestic and pleasure purposes. The issuing company is Wilson's Insurance and the cover note number is MOT543654.

The driver then hands you a paper and photocard driving licence relating to Aaron Stringer. Upon examination of the documents you note that the driver number is STRIN 804205 AG9DD. You also note that the driving licence is a provisional licence only for Category B cars. The car is not displaying 'L' plates and the driver was the only person in the vehicle.

 What do you know?

What do you need to do now?

What do you know?

* You have seen a motor vehicle being driven on a road by Aaron Stringer who is a provisional licence holder for that class of vehicle.

* You also know that as a provisional licence holder, the driver must display 'L' plates to the front and rear of the vehicle, and be supervised by a person who is at least 21 years old and who has held a current full licence for that class of vehicle for at least three years.

What do you need to do now?

As you suspect an offence has been committed, you must caution the driver and make a note of the time before asking any further questions and pointing out the offences.

At 09:20 hours, you now say to Aaron Stringer:

> You do not have to say anything. But it may harm your defence if you do not mention when questioned something which you later rely on in court. Anything you do say may be given in evidence.

You may now point out the offences and say:

As a provisional licence holder you must display 'L' plates to the front and rear of the vehicle and be supervised by a person at least 21 years old who has held a current full licence for this class of vehicle for at least three years. You are committing an offence of driving otherwise than in accordance with a licence.

To this he replies:

I'm sorry, I know. I've got my test in a couple of weeks and just wanted to get in some extra practice.

You can now report the driver for the offence by saying:

You will be reported for the offence of driving otherwise than in accordance with a licence.

You should also caution the driver using the following version:

You do not have to say anything. But it may harm your defence if you do not mention *now* something which you later rely on in court. Anything you do say may be given in evidence.

The driver makes no reply. If a driver makes any reply, this must be recorded.

It is also worth noting that the insurance cover for this vehicle may be invalidated because the driver does not hold a full licence and is not being supervised by a competent driver. If so, the driver commits another offence (of using the vehicle without a valid certificate of insurance).

In this situation you need to advise the driver that in driving now he will be continuing to commit the offence and that he should not drive the vehicle until he can comply with conditions as stipulated.

Aaron Stringer decides to lock the vehicle and return with his older brother later to collect it.

You now need to write up the incident in your pocket notebook. An example of this follows:

09:15   I was on foot patrol in High Street, Castleton when I saw a Green Peugeot motor vehicle, index S456 JAD, being driven towards Church Lane. The vehicle then parked on its nearside outside J's Newsagents. My attention was drawn to the vehicle as I could hear loud music coming from the vehicle, which appeared to be disturbing passers-by. I approached the vehicle and spoke to the driver, the only occupant, whom I now believe to be Aaron Gavin STRINGER, date of birth 20.04.85, of Flat 2, Peak Towers, Whatley Street, Castleton CL1 3KR. I informed him that the music was being played too loudly and was upsetting passers-by, at which he turned the radio off. I said 'Are you the owner of this car?', to which he replied stating he had bought the car two days ago for £200. I examined the 'New Keeper Supplement' with Stringer's details entered into the New Keeper's name and address section. I then said 'May I see your driving licence, insurance certificate and MOT certificate?' I then examined the MOT certificate, which I found to be in order. I also examined an insurance cover note issued by Wilson's Insurance, cover note no MOT543654, which appeared to be in order.

STRINGER then handed to me a paper and photocard driving licence in his name with driver number STRIN 804205 AG9DD. I also noted that the licence was a provisional licence only for Category B cars. The car was not displaying 'L' plates and Stringer was the only occupant.

At 09:20 hours, I said to STRINGER, 'You do not have to say anything. But it may harm your defence if you do not mention when questioned something which you later rely on in court. Anything you do say may be given in evidence. As a provisional licence holder you must display 'L' plates to the front and rear of the vehicle and be supervised by a person at least 21 years old who has held a current full licence for this class of vehicle for at least three years. You are committing an offence of driving otherwise than in accordance with a licence.'

STRINGER replied, 'I'm sorry, I know. I've got my test in a couple of weeks and just wanted to get in some extra practice.'

I said, 'You will be reported for the offence of driving otherwise than in accordance with a licence. You do not have to say anything. But it may harm your defence if you do not mention now something which you later rely on in court. Anything you do say may be given in evidence.'

STRINGER made no reply.

> I advised STRINGER that in driving now he would be continuing to commit the offence and that he should not drive the vehicle until he can comply with conditions as stipulated.
>
> STRINGER decided to lock the vehicle and return later to collect it with his older brother.
>
> 09:25   Return to Castleton Police Station.
>
> Pocket notebook re above entry completed in Report Room.

In accordance with your local force policy you will be required to complete a Statement of Evidence based upon your pocket notebook entry. This will form part of the file for a summons to be processed.

Power to require production of documents

Driving licence

Section 164 of the Road Traffic Act 1988 provides a constable with the power to demand production of a driving licence.

The following people may be required to produce their driving licences for examination, to enable a constable to ascertain the name and address of the licence holder, the date of issue of the licence and the issuing authority:

- a person driving a motor vehicle on a road (or the supervisor of a provisional licence holder);

- a person whom you have reasonable cause to believe to have been the driver of a motor vehicle at the time when an accident occurred owing to its presence on a road;

- a person whom you have reasonable cause to believe to have committed an offence in relation to the use of a motor vehicle on a road; or

- a person whom you have reasonable cause to believe was supervising the holder of a provisional licence when an accident occurred, or at a time when an offence was suspected of having been committed by the provisional licence holder in relation to the use of the vehicle on a road.

Certificate of insurance and test certificate

Section 165 of the Road Traffic Act 1988 provides a constable with the power to demand production of a relevant certificate of insurance and test certificate.

As a constable you may require the following people to produce their certificate of insurance and test certificate (if applicable) for examination:

◆ a person driving a motor vehicle on a road (other than an invalid carriage); or

◆ a person whom you have reasonable cause to believe to have been the driver of a motor vehicle at a time when an accident occurred owing to its presence on a road or other public place; or

◆ a person whom you have reasonable cause to believe to have committed an offence in relation to the use of a motor vehicle on a road (other than an invalid carriage).

That person must also give:

◆ his or her name and address; and

◆ the name and address of the owner of the vehicle.

Other offences

Section 87 of the Road Traffic Act 1988 defines the offence of driving otherwise than in accordance with a licence:

(1) It is an offence for a person to drive on a road a motor vehicle of any class otherwise than in accordance with a licence authorising him to drive a motor vehicle of that class.

This offence applies when a person holds a particular licence and fails to comply with the conditions of the licence. For example, a holder of a provisional licence driving a motor vehicle when not displaying 'L' plates and/or when not being supervised by the holder of a full driving licence.

Regulation 103 of the Road Vehicles (Construction and Use) Regulations 1986 defines the offence of causing an unnecessary obstruction of the road:

No person in charge of a motor vehicle or trailer shall cause or permit the vehicle to stand on a road so as to cause any unnecessary obstruction of the road.

Chapter 6
Domestic Violence

This chapter covers the following units of the National Occupational Standards for Policing (level 3):

1A1 Use police actions in a fair and justified way.

1A4 Foster people's equality, diversity and rights.

2C1 Provide initial response to incidents.

2C3 Arrest, detain or report individuals.

2C4 Minimise and deal with aggressive and abusive behaviour.

2H1 Interview victims and witnesses.

2K2 Present detained persons to custody.

4G2 Ensure your own actions reduce risks to health and safety.

Introduction

Domestic violence is a serious problem that has an impact on everyone involved.

What is domestic violence?

Any incident of threatening behaviour, violence or abuse (psychological, physical, sexual, financial or emotional) between adults (aged 18 or over) who are or who have been intimate partners regardless of gender. It will also include family members who are defined as mother, father, son, daughter, brother, sister, grandparents, in-laws and step family. (ACPO/Home Office/CPS definition)

Domestic homicide statistics

England and Wales (1990–2001): average number of deaths per annum

	Murder victims	*Domestic murder victims*	*Partner/ex-partner homicides*
Male	403 (63.5%)	81 (20%)	28 (7% total men murdered)
Female	230 (36.5%)	141 (61%)	97 (42% total women murdered)
Total	633	222 (35% of total)	125 (20% total homicides)

The scenario

It is 23:15 hours on a Friday night. You are on mobile patrol with a colleague when you receive a call from the communications centre, directing you to attend 47 Carnforth Gardens, Castleshire. BT received an incomplete 999 call from this address. The call was described as being from a woman screaming for help. The handset was replaced before an address was given. BT has obtained the address by tracing the call.

 What do you know?

What do you need to know?

How are you going to find that out?

What next?

What do you know?

- At 23:15 hours today an incomplete telephone call was received from a female caller screaming for help.

- The handset was replaced prior to any information being given.

- The call has been traced to 47 Carnforth Gardens, Castleshire.

What do you need to know?

- Is there any further information?

- Is there any information about previous incidents at this address?

- What is the location of Carnforth Gardens?

How are you going to find that out?

- The communication centre may be able to give some more information.

- There may be some historic information relating to 47 Carnforth Gardens on the computerised information system, or from some other officer who is currently on duty.

- If you do not know where Carnforth Gardens is, ask the communication centre to give you directions.

What next?

Acknowledge the call and make your way to 47 Carnforth Gardens.

On arrival at the address, inform the communications centre that you have arrived at the scene. It may need this information to update the time it has taken to respond to the call. It also needs to be aware you have arrived at the scene for reasons to do with your health and safety. It may also have obtained further information about the incident in the time it has taken you to travel to the scene.

The communication centre informs you that there is a history of domestic violence at the property. The last call was 6 weeks ago, when an arrest was made at the premises for a breach of the peace. The person arrested at that time was Paul Barron, one of the registered occupants of the premises.

What next?

You and your partner knock on the door of the premises; a man opens the door and asks you what you want. You say that there has been an incomplete 999 call from this address and that you need to check it out. You ask him if you can enter the premises to check on the well-being of the occupants.

The man says that he has no idea what you are talking about and that nobody has used the telephone that evening.

The man immediately becomes aggressive and refuses to allow you to enter the premises. He states that it is far too late at night, and says that if you return in the morning he will talk to you.

 What do you know?

What do you need to know?

How are you going to find that out?

What next?

What do you know?

+ You know there has been an incomplete emergency 999 call which has been traced to this address.

+ You know the person on the telephone line was female.

+ You know that the man who has answered the door does not want to give you access to the premises.

+ You know that he has become aggressive immediately.

What do you need to know?

Are you at the right address; is it possible that you are at the wrong premises?

How are you going to find that out?

You check with the communications centre to verify that the address you have attended is the correct address.

The communications centre confirms that you are at the right address.

What next?

You know that you have to gain entry to the premises to check on the well-being of the occupants. At this time you have no knowledge of how many occupants there are, or who they are.

 What do you need to know?

How are you going to find that out?

What next?

What do you need to know?

- Do you have any right of entry to the premises?
- If so, what are your powers of entry?
- Has there been a breach of the peace?
- If so, it is your duty to prevent any action likely to result in a breach of the peace in both public and private places.

Under common law a constable may arrest without warrant any person:

(a) who is committing a breach of the peace;

(b) who he or she reasonably believes will commit a breach of the peace in the immediate future; or

(c) who has committed a breach of the peace where it is reasonably believed that a recurrence of the breach of the peace is threatened.

The constable must have a genuine belief that there is a real and imminent risk of a breach of the peace occurring.

You do not have evidence that a breach of the peace is being committed, or has been or will be committed, so what other powers do you have?

Under s 17(1)(b) of the Police and Criminal Evidence Act (PACE) 1984 (see **Appendix**), a constable may enter any premises for the purpose of arresting a person for an indictable offence.

Do you know if an arrestable offence has been committed? You do not have that information, so s 17(1)(b) does not apply.

You do have concerns for the safety of the woman who made the initial call. Do you know if she is safe and well?

How are you going to find that out?

The only way you are going to ensure the well-being of the female caller is by gaining entry to the premises.

Under s 17(1)(g) of PACE 1984 (see **Appendix**), a constable may enter premises for the purpose of saving life or limb, or for preventing serious damage to property. Ensuring the well-being of the female caller would fall within s 17(1)(g).

What next?

You have the power to enter the premises; your next course of action is gaining entry. You again speak to the man at the door. You inform him that you need to speak to the woman who made the phone call; you have to verify that everything is all right with everybody concerned.

You ask the man for his details; at first he refuses to give them to you, but you engage him in conversation, you calm him down by being reasonable, and he starts to talk to you. He gives his name as Paul Barron.

What next?

You continue to talk to Barron and inform him that you have the power to enter the premises but you would rather enter at his invitation. Whatever happens, you need to see that the other occupants of the premises are fit and well.

Due to your communication style you have calmed Paul Barron down; he invites you into the premises, so you have not needed to use the powers of entry granted to you under legislation.

You and your colleague follow Barron into the living room of the premises.

What next?

What are your priorities at a possible domestic violence incident once you have secured lawful entry?

Your first priority is to protect all persons from injury. This includes you and your colleague. Generally, in order to ensure this you need to split up the parties involved and take control of the incident. Be careful where you go in the house. For example, it is not good practice to take a potentially aggressive individual into the kitchen. In the kitchen there are many items which may be used as weapons.

You follow Paul Barron into the living room of the premises. A woman is sitting on the settee. She looks as if she has been crying and her hair is dishevelled, but there are no visible injuries. Barron sits beside her, which appears to make her anxious. You ask her for her name, and she tells you that she is Penny Wells. You ask her if she is all right, and she nods and says 'Yes'.

You are not happy about the situation and decide you want to talk to Penny Wells away from Paul Barron. He appears to be trying to intimidate her with his presence. You need to find out if there are other occupants in the house and if they are fit and well.

You ask Penny to come into the hallway to talk to you, and you ask your colleague to talk to Paul. As soon as you try to get Penny by herself, Paul Barron becomes agitated and gets to his feet, stopping Penny from moving.

What next?

You need to take control of the situation. You need to investigate what has happened. Penny Wells is obviously not comfortable and appears to be intimidated by Paul Barron.

87

You inform Paul that you need to speak to Penny by herself and will not leave the premises until you have done so. You ask Penny to go into the hallway, and stand between her and Paul to let her get past.

What are your considerations?

If an assault has taken place prior to your arrival, consider what the offender is likely to do if you are about to take some form of action:

◆ He might become violent and assault Penny Wells, you or your colleague.

◆ If he has committed an offence, he might try to leave the premises.

◆ There might be other persons on the premises whom he could assault or use to assist his escape.

Both you and your colleague need to be very aware of health and safety considerations for everybody involved.

What next?

You want to talk to Penny but do not want to leave your colleague in a vulnerable position. You get Penny as far away from the living room door as possible, but leave the door slightly open so as to be able to hear if there are any raised voices.

You ask Penny what has happened. At first she says nothing, but when you ask her if she made the phone call she breaks down and says that she has been assaulted by Paul. She tells you that she is terrified of him, but she stays because they have two children and he has threatened to hurt her if she leaves with the children.

Penny shows you her upper arms, which are red and beginning to bruise; she tells you that Paul has been dragging her about by her hair, kicking her in the back and upper legs, and has told her to say nothing to the police. She says that she cannot stand it anymore and she wants to leave with her two children. She tells you that her back and upper thighs are covered in bruises where he has hit and kicked her, but he is careful not to hit her where it shows. She also tells you the assaults have been going on for some time, and that they are getting more frequent and more severe.

What next?

Do you have enough evidence to arrest Paul Barron?

What do you know?

What do you need to know?

What next?

What do you know?

You have seen the bruising on Penny Wells's upper arms and she has informed you that her attacker was Barron. Do you have reasonable suspicion that an offence has been committed?

Under s 24 of PACE 1984 (see **Appendix**), a constable may arrest any person who is suspected of having committed an offence, or who is about to commit one.

Officers have discretion within a power of arrest not to use that power for a particular incident, where they believe it is not necessary or proportionate. Every such decision must be justified and documented in the same detailed way as a decision to use the power of arrest, but in domestic violence situations the presumption is towards arrest where lawful, necessary and justifiable.

If you do not arrest an offender at a domestic violence incident:

(a) be prepared to justify your decision;

(b) make a detailed written record as to why you have not arrested;

(c) explain the reason to the victim;

(d) reassure the victim that every step will be taken to –

  (i) prevent a recurrence,

  (ii) offer help, advice and protection.

Police services run a positive action policy in relation to domestic violence. Arrest would normally be the appropriate form of action wherever the power exists.

You can arrest without a complaint from the victim provided you have evidence of an offence (with a power of arrest) and reasonable grounds to believe that the alleged offender is responsible.

What do you need to know?

What offence or offences could you consider?

(a) At this moment you do not know the extent of Penny Wells's injuries.

There could be an offence of harassment contrary to the Protection from Harassment Act 1997. For this offence to be made out the harassment has to have occurred on more than one occasion.

(b) There appears to have been an assault on Penny Wells. You are unable to verify the extent of her injuries at the present time, but the assault could range from:

(i) common assault/battery (Criminal Justice Act 1988, s 39); to

(ii) assault occasioning actual bodily harm (Offences Against the Person Act 1861, s 47); to

(iii) wounding or inflicting grievous bodily harm (Offences Against the Person Act 1861, s 20); to

(iv) wounding or causing grievous bodily harm with intent (Offences Against the Person Act 1861, s18).

You decide you have a reasonable suspicion that the offence of assault occasioning actual bodily harm has occurred. You make the decision to arrest Barron.

What next?

You return to the living room where your colleague is still talking to Barron, who appears to be very agitated.

What are your main considerations?

You must be very aware of health and safety. If Barron becomes aggressive, is there anything he could use to hurt anyone in the house? You are aware that there are two children in the house: Where are they? Could Barron gain access to them or to Penny Wells?

What next?

You caution Barron and inform him of the grounds of his arrest – that you are arresting him on suspicion of committing assault occasioning actual bodily harm (Offences Against the Person Act 1861, s 47; see **Appendix**). Barron immediately tries to get past you to reach Penny Wells. You and your colleague restrain him and, using reasonable force, handcuff him for the journey to the police station.

You will need to make a note of the time of arrest and the reply given by Barron when he was cautioned, if he made any reply. In this case, he did not reply. The Custody Officer will require this information.

What next?

Get Penny out of the way of Barron; if possible get her to go upstairs to the children. Reassure her that you will be back to see her as soon as you have dealt with Barron.

The suspect is now in your care and custody. Under s 32 of PACE 1984 (see **Appendix**), if not at a police station you have the power to search persons who have been arrested if you have reasonable grounds for believing that they may:

(a) present a danger to themselves or others;

(b) have concealed on them anything which they might use to assist themselves to escape from lawful custody;

(c) have concealed on them anything which might be evidence relating to an offence.

You search Barron and are satisfied that he has no weapons or other items concealed on him which present a danger to you or to others.

What next?

Your prisoner needs to be transported to the police station as soon as possible, but you also need to see Penny Wells to let her know what is going to happen.

You have a dilemma – although Barron is handcuffed he still poses a threat as he is still agitated, but you need to keep Penny informed.

You contact the communications centre and ask if another officer, preferably female, could attend the address. You briefly outline the circumstances of the situation and of the arrest to the communications centre.

A female officer is on duty nearby and she will attend the premises within 5 minutes.

What next?

You quickly inform Penny Wells that a female officer is en route and will be with her within 5 minutes, and that you will take Barron to the police station and then return to see her. You check she is all right with this and that she is physically well and does not require any medical treatment. You briefly see the children, a boy of about 3 and a girl of about 5 – both appear to be unharmed. Penny informs you that Barron has never harmed the children.

 What do you know?

What do you need to know?

How are you going to find that out?

What next?

What do you know?

The suspect is in your custody. You are responsible for his safety and welfare in transferring him to the police station, until he has been accepted by the Custody Officer at the police station.

What do you need to know?

+ On arrival at the police station you need to make a note of the time. The Custody Officer will ask for this information.

+ You need to get full details from the arrested person. You know that his name is Paul Barron, but is that his full name? You need his date and place of birth, and to make a note of any distinguishing marks (such as scars or tattoos), which will ensure that the arrested person has been correctly identified.

+ You need to know if the arrested person has shown any warning signs, such as illness, self-harm or violence, both for his well-being and for that of the officers at the police station.

How are you going to find that out?

You now have enough details to carry out a check on the Police National Computer (PNC). All the details of persons convicted of recordable crimes are recorded on this system. You need to key in the person's full name, date of birth, sex, colour and height, known as the NASCH factors. You are able to conduct a search with fewer details, but the more information you put in, the more accurate the search will be. If you do not have the authority to carry out a (PNC) check, there will be staff at the station who will be able to do it for you.

What next?

You are now ready to take the arrested person through to the Custody Officer.

What do you know?

What do you need to know?

How are you going to find that out?

What next?

What do you know?

◆ It is the Custody Officer's responsibility to ensure that there are grounds to authorise the detention of the arrested person.

◆ The Custody Officer will want to know if you have searched the person. He will want a further search to be made, and at this time any articles which could be used to injure or damage the arrested person, any other person or property will be removed. This will include belts, laces and any other items of clothing that could be used to cause injury or damage.

- At this time you must be aware of cultural differences. If, for example, a person from the Sikh faith was arrested and his turban had to be removed for health and safety reasons, that person must be supplied with an alternative head covering whilst he is in custody. His turban must also be treated with respect and be stored in a clean place.

What do you need to know?

- You need to be able to give enough information to the Custody Officer for him to make a decision as to whether to authorise the detention of the arrested person.

- He also needs to be informed about any injuries or possible illnesses from which the arrested person may be suffering.

How are you going to find that out?

Having decided at the scene of the incident that you had a power of arrest, that the arrest was necessary and that you had reasonable grounds for suspecting that the person had committed the offence of s 47 assault, you need to give this information to the Custody Officer. The Custody Officer requires as much detail as possible in order to make an informed decision as to whether to authorise detention. The restriction of someone's liberty is a serious matter, and it is a decision which must not be taken lightly.

What next?

You need to have to hand the information the Custody Officer will require.

What information do you need to give to the Custody Officer?

- The time and place of the arrest.

- The details of the offence which gave you the grounds for the arrest.

- What property, if any, you have taken into your possession.

- Whether force was used during the arrest.

- Whether the arrested person was handcuffed.

- Your time of arrival at the police station with the arrested suspect.

From the information you have supplied the Custody Officer has to decide whether there are sufficient grounds and reasons to authorise the arrested person's detention at the police station. If detention is authorised it is the

Custody Officer's responsibility to ensure that the detainee is fit to be detained and interviewed. Detention will usually be authorised for the purposes of preserving and securing evidence, and to obtain evidence by way of questioning. This requires you to obtain and record the necessary evidence, eg your pocket note book, the injured person's statement and relevant witness statements. You will be required to carry out these tasks immediately, as the detainee must be interviewed as soon as practicable.

When a person is brought to a police station under arrest, or is arrested at the police station having gone there voluntarily, the Custody Officer must make sure that the person is told clearly about the following continuing rights which may be exercised at any stage during the period in custody:

(a) the right to have someone informed of their arrest;

(b) the right to consult privately with a solicitor and that free independent legal advice is available;

(c) the right to consult the Codes of Practice.

The Custody Officer has the responsibility for ensuring that the PACE Codes of Practice are adhered to.

What next?

Having had his detention authorised by the Custody Officer, Paul Barron is informed of his rights. He is offered access to free independent legal advice, which at this time he declines. He is informed that if at any time he wishes to have free independent legal advice, it will be arranged for him. He is then searched and, as mentioned above, property is removed from him, comprising a wallet containing an Egg credit card in his name, 3 × £10 Bank of England notes, 55 pence in loose change and 3 keys on a ring. This property is recorded with all the other information on the custody record sheet, which is completed by the Custody Officer.

The Custody Officer must also note on the custody record any comments the arrested person makes as to the arresting officers' account of the arrest, but he shall not invite comment.

 What do you need to know?

How are you going to find that out?

What next?

What do you need to know?

- Once the detention procedure is complete you need to obtain further information about the offence.
- You need to inform the Custody Officer about your future actions. He needs to be aware of what is happening in relation to persons who are in his custody.

How are you going to find that out?

You need to return to 47 Carnforth Gardens to see Penny Wells. You need to do this for several reasons:

(a) to continue the investigation;

(b) to reassure Penny that she is safe as Paul Barron is in custody;

(c) to verify the extent of her injuries and to check on the welfare of the children.

What next?

On your arrival at 47 Carnforth Gardens you speak to your female colleague, who informs you that Penny Wells has extensive bruising to her upper thighs and back. Penny also states that she is terrified of Barron returning now that she has made a complaint against him.

What are your considerations?

You have to investigate the crime that has been committed, but you must be mindful of the traumatic effect that domestic violence has upon victims and their families. It is particularly important to deal with victims sensitively and professionally.

Professionalism blends effective investigation of the facts with empathy and respect for those involved, to ensure that a positive relationship is established and maintained. One bad experience may make people reluctant to report any further incidents and undermines trust.

 What do you need to know?

How are you going to find that out?

What next?

What do you need to know?

◆ You need to know the details of the assault and, if possible, ascertain the severity of the injuries. This will have a bearing on what offence the offender will be charged with.

◆ You need to obtain statements from the injured person and any other witnesses to the assault. In this case the only witness is Penny Wells. The children did not see the assault.

How are you going to find that out?

You should always consider enhanced evidence gathering. For enhanced evidence gathering you should consider:

◆ speaking to neighbours, friends or (in some cases) work colleagues;

◆ speaking to any other potential witnesses;

◆ preserving 999 tapes;

◆ if applicable, preserving any CCTV footage;

◆ preserving forensic evidence;

◆ interviewing children in the household. You must comply with the document 'Achieving best evidence in criminal proceedings' in relation to interviewing children. Always bear in mind that the welfare of the children is paramount;

- making use of any call recording, intelligence systems or crime recording systems your force may have. Check for any previous incidents, bail conditions, injunctions or restraining orders;

- if applicable, arranging a medical examination of the victim. In some cases it is advisable also to have the offender medically examined.

All the above are obviously dependent on the nature of the offence you are investigating and on the sensitivities of the investigation.

What next?

Statements should be obtained as soon as practicable after the event, when the witness will be best able to recall the incident. You must always be aware, however, of the well-being of the victim. It is now 00:50 hours and Penny Wells has been waiting for your return. She is terrified that Paul Barron will return and hurt her now that she has informed the police of the assault. She tells you she is not going to remain in the house with the children. She also says that she wants to give her statement to the female officer who is with her now rather than to you.

What are your considerations?

You need to investigate this offence and obtain the necessary information to put before the court, but you also need to look to the welfare of the victim and her children.

In practical terms, will the victim be able to concentrate on giving a full statement whist she is thinking of the welfare of her children and herself, and whilst she is still at the address where she was assaulted?

 What do you know?

What do you need to know?

How are you going to find that out?

What next?

What do you know?

- You know that there has been an assault and that the victim is concerned for her and her children's future safety.

- You know the person responsible for the assault is in custody, but you do not know how long he will remain in custody.

- You know that you require a statement of evidence from the victim and that she would like a female officer to take that statement.

What do you need to know?

Where can Penny Wells and her children stay? Have they some family member they can go to, or will they require assistance from the social services or a women's refuge organisation?

How are you going to find that out?

You speak to Penny about future accommodation for her and the children. Penny informs you that her parents live nearby. She would be welcomed there with the children, and she would be safe as Barron would not touch her whilst she was there. The only reason she had not gone before was that each time Barron assaulted her he promised it would be the last time. She is determined now to make a break from Barron for the sake of the children.

What next?

You need to assist Penny Wells to get to her parents' home. Penny phones her parents, and her father agrees to come round immediately to collect her and the children. As previously mentioned, a statement is required from Penny about the current assault and any prior assaults. Your female colleague has built up a rapport with Penny Wells, and to continue this she states that she will stay and assist Penny in gathering belongings to take to her parents' address. She will also arrange an appointment to see Penny as soon as possible (the same day) in order to obtain a witness statement from her. You explain to Penny that Barron is in custody and that you are returning to see the Custody Officer to arrange to have Barron detained for court in the morning.

What next?

The welfare of the victim and her children has been taken care of for the moment.

You now need to return to see the Custody Officer for advice regarding Barron's court appearance. If the Custody Officer agrees with this course of action, you need to interview Barron, and you and your colleagues need to write statements and complete a file of evidence to put before the court. If this was not a domestic incident the Custody Officer would be more likely to bail the suspect to return to the police station at a future date in order for you to complete your enquiries. Because of the nature of this incident you will put Barron before the court to ask either for a remand application, or for bail conditions to prevent him molesting the victim.

What next?

You need to plan your interview. (For PEACE interviewing of suspects, see **Chapter 2**, Burglary.)

When interviewing the suspect you should plan your interview to include questions relating to the history of the relationship with the victim, bringing in the opportunity to comment upon any known previous instances of violence.

What next?

You and your colleague interview Barron. He is remorseful and admits the offence of s 47 assault. You obtain all the information you can using the PEACE model of interviewing.

You and your colleague complete statements of evidence. Police statements are potentially excellent sources of evidence. The quality and accuracy of your statements will be crucial. You should seek to include details that evidence:

(a) the nature of the victim's distress;

(b) the victim's injuries;

(c) the suspect's injuries (if applicable);

(d) any damage to property;

(e) your observations of the scene, eg overturned furniture, property lying about, damaged ornaments, etc;

(f) the suspect's demeanour, eg angry, aggressive, threatening, passive, unco-operative;

(g) the victim's demeanour, eg scared, angry, terrified, passive, upset;

(h) allegations made by the victim in the presence of the suspect;

(i) any unsolicited comments made by the suspect.

What next?

After your interview and initial enquiries you take the information to the Custody Officer. He will decide whether you have enough evidence to charge the suspect. In this case the Custody Officer decides that there is enough evidence to charge the suspect with the offence of s 47 assault and to remand him for court in the morning.

What next?

You need to charge the suspect with the offence and complete the file of evidence to put before the court. The file is not complete at the present time as you have not yet obtained a statement from the witness. The file should contain as much evidence as possible so that the Crown Prosecution Service can lay the full facts before the court, which can then make a fully informed decision.

Guidance on the completion of files is given in the *Manual of Guidance for the preparation, processing and submission of files and the disclosure of materials 2002*, produced by ACPO and the CPS.

What next?

Once the file of evidence is as complete as possible, you should liaise with the Custody Officer to decide what course of action should be adopted with regard to a remand application or conditional bail application.

In view of the circumstances of the assault, the Custody Officer informs you that the best course of action is to apply for conditional bail.

Bail can be opposed or conditions attached if it appears that it is necessary to prevent the suspect from:

(a) failing to surrender to custody;

(b) committing an offence whilst on bail;

(c) interfering with witnesses or otherwise obstructing the course of justice, whether in relation to himself or any other person.

What next?

What bail conditions might you consider imposing to protect the victim in this case?

Conditions could state that the suspect must:

(a) not contact the victim either directly or indirectly;

(b) not go within a certain distance of the victim's place of residence or place of work;

(c) not go within a certain distance of specified schools or nurseries, or other places the victim or the children attend;

(d) live at a specified address;

(e) report to a named police station on specified days at specified times;

(f) obey any curfew justifiably imposed.

What next?

You have obtained all the information you can at the present time. You have your and your colleagues' statements. Barron has been charged with the offence of s 47 assault and remanded for court. You have completed the file and requested bail conditions for Barron.

What next?

You must remember that your work is not completed in relation to gathering evidence for this offence. Although Barron admitted the offence of assault when you interviewed him, you still need all the evidence to prove the offence.

Your colleague has arranged to obtain a statement from Penny Wells. She has also persuaded her to agree to her injuries being photographed by a scenes of crime officer, and you must arrange an appointment for her to attend as soon as possible.

In order to give the best support, the police service must maintain regular contact with victims or witnesses to keep them informed about developments within the case such as bail dates, the location of the offender and details of court appearances. In some cases this will be the responsibility of the officer in charge of the case; in others it will fall to specialist departments. You should always supply victims with details of specialist departments and other voluntary and statutory agencies that are in a position to help and provide support, regardless of whether criminal proceedings are pursued.

Your individual force will have policies in place for domestic violence incidents. It is important to pass relevant details to the communication centres in order for them to update the incident logs and code them correctly. If this is done, the relevant support departments within the force are informed of the incidents automatically. This will ensure that domestic violence units will have access to accurate data, which will enable them to follow up cases.

What information should you give to communications staff about a domestic incident before the log is closed? Force systems differ and you need to comply with your individual force's policies, but full details of the incident and of all parties involved should be recorded on the incident log in line with your force policy. Such details will include the names, dates of birth and home addresses of:

(a) victims;

(b) suspects;

(c) witnesses;

(d) children.

It is also important to record whether a suspect was arrested and under what power, and any justification for not making an arrest.

Your force may also want you to complete a separate domestic violence report.

The domestic violence officer should be informed of all domestic violence incidents. This may be the responsibility of the communications centre staff, the domestic violence officer, or you as the officer in charge of the case. Check and make yourself aware of your individual force policy.

Appendix
Legislation

Theft

Theft Act 1968

1. (1) A person is guilty of theft if he dishonestly appropriates property belonging to another with the intention of permanently depriving the other of it ...

Burglary

Theft Act 1968

9. (1) A person is guilty of burglary if—
    (a) he enters any building or part of a building as a trespasser and with intent to commit any such offence as is mentioned in subsection (2) below; or
    (b) having entered any building or part of a building as a trespasser he steals or attempts to steal anything in the building or that part of it or attempts to inflict on any person therein any grievous bodily harm.

    (2) The offences referred to in subsection (1)(a) above are offences of stealing anything in the building or part of a building in question, of inflicting on any person therein any grievous bodily harm, and of doing unlawful damage to the building or anything therein.

Power of arrest

Police and Criminal Evidence Act 1984 (as amended by Senior Organised Crime and Police Act 2005)

24. (1) A constable may arrest without a warrant—
    (a) anyone who is about to commit an offence;
    (b) anyone who is in the act of committing an offence;
    (c) anyone whom he has reasonable grounds for suspecting to be about to commit an offence;
    (d) anyone whom he has reasonable grounds for suspecting to be committing an offence.

(2) If a constable has reasonable grounds for suspecting that an offence has been committed, he may arrest without a warrant anyone whom he has reasonable grounds to suspect of being guilty of it.

(3) If an offence has been committed, a constable may arrest without a warrant—
(a) anyone who is guilty of the offence;
(b) anyone whom he has reasonable grounds for suspecting to be guilty of it.

(4) But the power of summary arrest conferred by subsection (1), (2) or (3) is exercisable only if the constable has reasonable grounds for believing that for any of the reasons mentioned in subsection (5) it is necessary to arrest the person in question.

(5) The reasons are—
(a) to enable the name of the person in question to be ascertained (in the case where the constable does not know, and cannot readily ascertain, the person's name, or has reasonable grounds for doubting whether a name given by the person as his name is his real name);
(b) correspondingly as regards the person's address;
(c) to prevent the person in question—
(i) causing physical injury to himself or any other person;
(ii) suffering physical injury;
(iii) causing loss of or damage to property;
(iv) committing an offence against public decency (subject to subsection (6)); or
(v) causing an unlawful obstruction of the highway;
(d) to protect a child or other vulnerable person from the person in question;
(e) to allow the prompt and effective investigation of the offence or of the conduct of the person in question;
(f) to prevent any prosecution for the offence from being hindered by the disappearance of the person in question.

(6) Subsection (5)(c)(iv) applies only where members of the public going about their normal business cannot reasonably be expected to avoid the person in question.

Search and seizure

Police and Criminal Evidence Act 1984 (as amended by the Senior Organised Crime and Police Act 2005)

17. (1) a constable may enter and search any premises for the purpose—

(a) of executing—

(i) a warrant of arrest issued in connection with or arising out of criminal proceedings, or

(ii) a warrant of commitment issued under section 76 of the Magistrates' Courts Act 1980;

(b) of arresting a person for an indictable offence;

(c) of arresting a person for an offence under—

(i) section 1 (prohibition of uniforms in connection with political objects) ... of the Public Order Act 1936;

(ii) any enactment contained in section 6 to 8 or 10 of the Criminal Law Act 1977 (offences relating to entering and remaining on property);

(iii) section 4 of the Public Order Act 1986 (fear or provocation of violence);

(iiia) section 4 (driving etc when under influence of drink or drugs) or 163 (failure to stop when required to do so by a constable in uniform) of the Road Traffic Act 1988;

(iv) section 76 of the Criminal Justice and Public Order Act 1994 (failure to comply with an interim possession order);

(ca) of arresting, in pursuance of section 32(1A) of the Children and Young Persons Act 1969, any child or young person who has been remanded or committed to local authority accommodation under section 23(1) of that Act;

(cb) of recapturing any person who is, or is deemed for any purpose to be, unlawfully at large while liable to be detained—

(i) in a prison, remand centre, young offender institution or secure training centre; or

(ii) in pursuance of section 92 of the Powers of Criminal Courts (Sentencing) Act 2000 (dealing with children and young persons guilty of grave crimes) in any other place;

(d) of recapturing any person whatever who is unlawfully at large and whom he is pursuing; or

(e) of saving life or limb or preventing serious damage to property.

18. (1) a constable may enter and search any premises occupied or controlled by a person who is under arrest for an indictable offence, if he has reasonable grounds for suspecting that there is on the premises evidence, other than items subject to legal privilege, that relates—
(a) to that offence; or
(b) to some other indictable offence which is connected with or similar to that offence.

(2) A constable may seize and retain anything for which he may search under subsection (1) above.

(3) The power to search conferred by subsection (1) above is only a power to search to the extent that is reasonably required for the purpose of discovering such evidence.

(4) Subject to subsection (5) below, the powers conferred by this section may not be exercised unless an officer of the rank of inspector or above has authorised them in writing.

(5) A constable may conduct a search under subsection (1)—
(a) before the person is taken to a police station or released on bail under section 30A, and
(b) without obtaining an authorisation under subsection (4), if the condition in subsection (5A) is satisfied.

(5A) The condition is that the presence of the person at a place (other than a police station) is necessary for the effective investigation of the offence.

(6) If a constable conducts a search by virtue of subsection (5) above, he shall inform an officer of the rank of inspector or above that he has made the search as soon as practicable after he has made it.

(7) An officer who—
(a) authorises a search; or
(b) is informed of a search under subsection (6) above, shall make a record in writing—
(i) of the grounds for the search; and
(ii) of the nature of the evidence that was sought.

(8) If the person who was in occupation or control of the premises at the time of the search is in police detention at the time the record is to be made, the officer shall make the record as part of his custody record.

32. (1) A constable may search an arrested person, in any case where the person to be searched has been arrested at a place other than a police station, if the constable has reasonable grounds for believing that the arrested person may present a danger to himself or others.

(2) Subject to subsections (3) to (5) below, a constable shall also have power in any such case:

(a) to search the arrested person for anything—
    (i) which he might use to assist him to escape from lawful custody; or
    (ii) which might be evidence relating to an offence; and
(b) if the offence for which he has been arrested is an indictable offence, to enter and search any premises in which he was when arrested or immediately before he was arrested for evidence relating to the offence.

(3)   The power to search conferred by subsection (2) above is only a power to search to the extent that is reasonably required for the purpose of discovering any such thing or any such evidence.

(4)   The powers conferred by this section to search a person are not to be construed as authorising a constable to require a person to remove any of his clothing in public other than the outer coat, jacket or gloves but they do authorise a search of a person's mouth.

(5)   A constable may not search a person in the exercise of the power conferred by subsection (2)(b) above unless he has reasonable grounds for believing that the person to be searched may have concealed on him anything for which a search is permitted under that paragraph.

Offence of leaving litter

Environmental Protection Act 1990

87. (1) If any person throws down, drops or otherwise deposits in, into or from any place to which this section applies, and leaves, any thing whatsoever in such circumstances as to cause, or contribute to, or tend to lead to, the defacement by litter of any place to which this section applies he shall, subject to subsection (2) below, be guilty of an offence.

(2)   No offence is committed under this section where the depositing and leaving of the thing was—
(a) authorised by law, or
(b) done with the consent of the owner, occupier or other person or authority having control of the place in or into which that thing was deposited.

(3)   ...

(4)   In this section 'public open place' means a place in the open air to which the public are entitled or permitted to have access without payment; and any covered place open to the air on at least one side and available for public use shall be treated as a public open place.

Causing harassment, alarm or distress

Public Order Act 1986

5. (1) A person is guilty of an offence if he:

   (a) uses threatening, abusive or insulting words or behaviour, or disorderly behaviour, or

   (b) displays any writing, sign or other visible representation which is threatening, abusive or insulting, within the hearing or sight of a person likely to be caused harassment, alarm or distress thereby.

   (2) An offence under this section may be committed in a public or a private place, except that no offence is committed where the words or behaviour are used or the writing, sign or other visible representation is displayed by a person inside a dwelling and the other person is also inside that or another dwelling.

   (4) A constable may arrest a person without warrant if—

   (a) he engages in offensive conduct which a constable warns him to stop, and

   (b) he engages in further offensive conduct immediately or shortly after the warning.

Assault occasioning actual bodily harm

Offences Against the Person Act 1861

47. Whosoever shall be convicted upon an indictment of any assault occasioning actual bodily harm shall be lilable ... to be imprisoned for any term not exceeding five years.

Definitions

Road Traffic Act 1988

185. (1) In this Act—

   ...

   'motor vehicle' means ... a mechanically propelled vehicle intended or adapted for use on roads ...

192. (1) In this Act—

   ...

   'road', in relation to England and Wales, means any highway and any other road to which the public has access, and includes bridges over which a road passes ...

Index

111